OCR GCSE
Mathematics A

Higher Homework Book

Series Editor: Brian Seager

- Howard Baxter
- Mike Handbury
- Jean Matthews
- Colin White
- Ruth Crookes
- John Jeskins
- Brian Seager

DYNAMIC
LEARNING

HODDER
EDUCATION
AN HACHETTE UK COMPANY

Hachette UK's policy is to use papers that are natural, renewable and recyclable products and made from wood grown in sustainable forests. The logging and manufacturing processes are expected to conform to the environmental regulations of the country of origin.

Orders: please contact Bookpoint Ltd, 130 Milton Park, Abingdon, Oxon OX14 4SB. Telephone: (44) 01235 827720. Fax: (44) 01235 400454. Lines are open from 9 a.m. to 5 p.m., Monday to Saturday, with a 24-hour message-answering service. Visit our website at www.hoddereducation.co.uk.

© Howard Baxter, Ruth Crookes, Michael Handbury, John Jeskins, Jean Matthews, Mark Patmore, Brian Seager, Colin White, Eddie Wilde, 2010
First published in 2010 by
Hodder Education
An Hachette UK company
338 Euston Road,
London, NW1 3BH

Impression number   10 9 8 7 6 5 4
Year   2015   2014   2013

Cover photo Stankervich/Shutterstock
Typeset in 10pt Bembo by Pantek Arts Ltd, Maidstone, Kent
Printed in Great Britain by CPI Group (UK) Ltd, Croydon CRO 4YY

A catalogue record for this title is available from the British Library

ISBN: 978 1444 112 818

Contents

Introduction   iv

Unit A

1	Working with numbers	2
2	Algebra	4
3	Statistical diagrams	5
4	Equations	9
5	Ratio and proportion	10
6	Statistical calculations	13
7	Pythagoras' theorem	18
8	Formulae 1	21
9	Measures	23
10	Planning and collecting	25
11	Sequences	26
12	Constructions and loci	28
13	Sampling	30
14	Trigonometry	31
15	Representing and interpreting data	34
16	Formulae 2	42

Unit B

1	Properties of shapes	44
2	Fractions, decimals and percentages	47
3	Mental methods	50
4	Transformations	52
5	Straight-line graphs	57
6	Indices, decimals and surds	61
7	Inequalities	63
8	Congruency	64
9	Simultaneous equations	66
10	Vectors	68
11	Circle theorems	71
12	Scatter diagrams and time series	74

Unit C

1	Algebraic manipulation	78
2	Perimeter, area, volume and 2-D representation	80
3	Trial and improvement	85
4	Probability 1	86
5	Graphs 1	89
6	Measures	97
7	Percentage and proportional change	101
8	Standard form and using a calculator	104
9	Similarity	107
10	Factorising	110
11	Three-dimensional geometry	112
12	Proportion and variation	115
13	Graphs 2	118
14	Quadratic equations	120
15	Simultaneous equations	123
16	Trigonometry	124
17	Functions	128
18	Length, area and volume	131
19	Probability 2	137
20	Algebraic fractions	140

Introduction

About this book

This book contains exercises designed to be used for the Higher tier of GCSE Mathematics. It is particularly aimed at the OCR Specification A and each exercise matches one in the OCR Higher Student's Book.

In the Homework book, the corresponding exercises have the same number and end in H. Thus, for example, if you have been working on Similarity from Unit C in class and used Exercise 9.1, then the homework exercise is 9.1H. The homework exercises cover the same mathematics.

As in the Student's Book, most of the questions in Unit B are designed to be done without a calculator so that you can practise for the non-calculator paper. Also, many of the questions require problem-solving skills. These are indicated by this icon.

These homework exercises provide extra practice and are also in a smaller book to carry home! If you have understood the topics, you should be able to tackle these exercises confidently as they are no harder than those you have done in class and in some cases may be a little easier. See if you agree. More practice helps to reinforce the ideas you have learned and makes it easier to remember at a later stage.

Brian Seager
Series Editor

Unit A Contents

1   Working with numbers   2

2   Algebra   4

3   Statistical diagrams   5

4   Equations   9

5   Ratio and proportion   10

6   Statistical calculations   13

7   Pythagoras' theorem   18

8   Formulae 1   21

9   Measures   23

10 Planning and collecting   25

11 Sequences   26

12 Constructions and loci   28

13 Sampling   30

14 Trigonometry   31

15 Representing and interpreting data   34

16 Formulae 2   42

Unit B   43

Unit C   77

Working with numbers

Exercise 1.1H

1 Find the square of each of these numbers.
  (a) 20   **(b)** 42   **(c)** 5.1
  (d) 60   **(e)** 0.9

2 Find the cube of each of these numbers.
  (a) 7   **(b)** 3.5   **(c)** 9.4
  (d) 20   **(e)** 100

3 Find the square roots of each of these numbers.
  Where necessary, give your answer correct to
  2 decimal places.
  (a) 900   **(b)** 75   **(c)** 284
  (d) 31 684   **(e)** 40 401

4 Find the cube root of each of these numbers.
  Where necessary, give your answer correct to
  2 decimal places.
  (a) 729   **(b)** 144   **(c)** 9.261
  (d) 4848   **(e)** 100 000

5 A square has an area of 80 cm^2.
  What is the length of one side?
  Give your answer correct to 2 decimal places.

6 Work these out. Where necessary, give your
  answer correct to 2 decimal places.
  (a) 5.3^4 **(b)** 0.72^5 **(c)** 1.03^7
  (d) 1.37^6

7 Work these out. Where necessary, give your
  answer correct to 2 decimal places.
  (a) $\sqrt[4]{28561}$ **(b)** $\sqrt[5]{9.23}$
  (c) $\sqrt[4]{93}$ **(d)** $\sqrt[7]{2187}$

Exercise 1.2H

1 Write down the reciprocal of each of these
  numbers.
  (a) 4   **(b)** 9   **(c)** 65
  (d) 10   **(e)** 4.5

2 Write down the numbers of which these are the
  reciprocals.
  (a) $\frac{1}{6}$ **(b)** $\frac{1}{10}$ **(c)** $\frac{1}{25}$
  (d) $\frac{1}{71}$ **(e)** $\frac{2}{15}$

3 Write down the reciprocal of each of these
  numbers.
  Give your answers as fractions or mixed numbers.
  (a) $\frac{3}{5}$ **(b)** $\frac{4}{9}$ **(c)** $2\frac{2}{5}$
  (d) $5\frac{1}{3}$ **(e)** $\frac{3}{100}$

4 Find the reciprocal of each of these numbers.
  Give your answers as decimals.
  (a) 25   **(b)** 0.2   **(c)** 6.4
  (d) 625   **(e)** 0.16

Exercise 1.3H

1 Work out these.
  (a) $\frac{3}{4} + \frac{1}{6}$ **(b)** $\frac{5}{8} - \frac{2}{7}$ **(c)** $\frac{5}{9} \times \frac{3}{8}$
  (d) $\frac{7}{16} \div \frac{5}{12}$ **(e)** $1\frac{4}{5} + 2\frac{3}{4}$ **(f)** $6\frac{3}{7} - 2\frac{1}{3}$
  (g) $5\frac{3}{5} \times 4$ **(h)** $4\frac{5}{9} \div 1\frac{1}{6}$

2 Write these fractions in their lowest terms.
  (a) $\frac{40}{125}$ **(b)** $\frac{28}{49}$ **(c)** $\frac{72}{192}$
  (d) $\frac{225}{350}$ **(e)** $\frac{17}{153}$

3 Write these improper fractions as mixed numbers.
  (a) $\frac{120}{72}$ **(b)** $\frac{150}{13}$ **(c)** $\frac{86}{19}$
  (d) $\frac{192}{54}$ **(e)** $\frac{302}{17}$

Exercise 1.4H

Work out these on your calculator without writing
down the answers to the middle stages.
If the answers are not exact, give them correct to
2 decimal places.

1 $\dfrac{7.3 + 8.5}{5.7}$ **2** $\dfrac{158 + 1027}{125}$

3 $\dfrac{6.7 + 19.5}{12.2 - 5.7}$

4 $\sqrt{128 - 34.6}$

5 $5.7 + \dfrac{1.89}{0.9}$

6 $(12.6 - 9.8)^2$

7 $\dfrac{8.9}{2.3 \times 5.6}$

8 $\dfrac{15.4}{2.3^2}$

9 $10.9 \times (7.2 - 5.8)$

10 $\dfrac{4.8 \times 6.2}{5.2 \times 6.5}$

11 $\dfrac{7.1}{\sqrt{15.3 \times 0.6}}$

12 $\dfrac{3 - \sqrt{2.73 + 5.1}}{4}$

Exercise 1.5H

1 Work out these.
Round your answers to 1 decimal place.
(a) 6.7×7.6 (b) 640×0.078

2 Round each of these numbers to 1 significant figure.
(a) 14.3 (b) 38 (c) 6.54
(d) 308 (e) 1210 (f) 0.78
(g) 0.61 (h) 0.053 (i) 2413.5
(j) 0.0097

3 Round each of these numbers to 1 significant figure.
(a) 8.4 (b) 18.36 (c) 725
(d) 8032 (e) 98.3 (f) 0.71
(g) 0.0052 (h) 0.019 (i) 407.511
(j) 23 095

4 (a) Use rounding to 1 significant figure to estimate the answer to each of these calculations. Show your working.
(i) 21.2^3
(ii) 189×0.31
(iii) $\sqrt{11.1^2 - 4.8^2}$
(iv) $\dfrac{51.8 + 39.2}{0.022}$

(b) Use your calculator to find the correct answer to each of the calculations in (a). Where appropriate, round your answer to a sensible degree of accuracy.

Exercise 1.6H

Write each of these numbers as a product of its prime factors.

1 14
2 16
3 28
4 35
5 42
6 49
7 108
8 156
9 225
10 424

Exercise 1.7H

For each of these pairs of numbers
• write the numbers as products of their prime factors.
• state the highest common factor.
• state the lowest common multiple.

1 6 and 8
2 8 and 18
3 15 and 25
4 36 and 48
5 25 and 55
6 33 and 55
7 54 and 72
8 30 and 40
9 45 and 63
10 24 and 50

Exercise 1.8H

Work out these.

1 2×3
2 -5×8
3 -6×-2
4 -4×6
5 5×-7
6 -3×7
7 -4×-5
8 $28 \div -7$
9 $-25 \div 5$
10 $-20 \div 4$
11 $24 \div 6$
12 $-15 \div -3$
13 $-35 \div 7$
14 $64 \div -8$
15 $27 \div -9$
16 $3 \times 6 \div -9$
17 $-42 \div -7 \times -3$
18 $5 \times 6 \div -10$
19 $-9 \times 4 \div -6$
20 $-5 \times 6 \times -4 \div -8$

Exercise 2.1H

Expand these.

1 $7(3a + 6b)$

2 $5(2c + 3d)$

3 $4(3e - 5f)$

4 $3(7g - 2h)$

5 $3(4i + 2j - 3k)$

6 $3(5m - 2n + 3p)$

7 $6(4r - 3s - 2t)$

8 $8(4r + 2s + t)$

9 $4(3u + 5v)$

10 $6(4w + 3x)$

11 $2(5y + z)$

12 $4(3y + 2z)$

13 $5(3v + 2)$

14 $3(7 + 4w)$

15 $5(1 - 3a)$

16 $3(8g - 5)$

17 $x(2y + 3)$

18 $t(4 - 3p)$

19 $a(5b - 6c + 7d)$

20 $x(1 - x)$

Exercise 2.2H

Expand the brackets and simplify these.

1 (a) $3(4a + 5) + 2(3a + 4)$
   (b) $5(4b + 3) + 3(2b + 1)$
   (c) $2(3 + 6c) + 4(5 + 7c)$

2 (a) $2(4x + 5) + 3(5x - 2)$
   (b) $4(3y + 2) + 5(3y - 2)$
   (c) $3(4 + 7z) + 2(3 - 5z)$

3 (a) $4(4s + 3t) + 5(2s + 3t)$
   (b) $3(4v + 5w) + 2(3v + 2w)$
   (c) $6(2x + 5y) + 3(4x + 2y)$
   (d) $2(5v + 4w) + 3(2v + w)$

4 (a) $5(2n + 5p) + 4(2n - 5p)$
   (b) $3(4q + 6r) + 5(2q - 3r)$
   (c) $7(3d + 2e) + 5(3d - 2e)$
   (d) $5(3f + 8g) + 4(3f - 9g)$
   (e) $4(5h - 6j) - 6(2h - 5j)$
   (f) $4(5k - 6m) - 3(2k - 5m)$

Exercise 2.3H

Factorise these.

1 (a) $8x + 20$ (b) $3x + 6$
   (c) $9x - 12$ (d) $5x - 30$

2 (a) $16 + 8x$ (b) $9 + 15x$
   (c) $12 - 16x$ (d) $8 - 12x$

3 (a) $4x^2 + 16x$ (b) $6x^2 + 30x$
   (c) $8x^2 - 20x$ (d) $9x^2 - 15x$

Exercise 2.4H

Simplify each of the following, writing your answer using index notation.

1 (a) $7 \times 7 \times 7 \times 7 \times 7$
   (b) $3 \times 3 \times 3 \times 3 \times 3$
   (c) $2 \times 2 \times 2 \times 2 \times 2 \times 2$

2 (a) $d \times d \times d \times d \times d \times d \times d$
   (b) $m \times m \times m \times m \times m \times m$
   (c) $t \times t \times t \times t \times t \times t \times t$

3 (a) $a \times a \times a \times a \times b \times b$
   (b) $c \times c \times c \times c \times d \times d \times d \times d \times d$
   (c) $r \times r \times r \times s \times s \times t \times t \times t \times t$

4 (a) $2x \times 3y \times 6z$
   (b) $2a \times 3b \times 4c$
   (c) $r \times 2s \times 3t \times 4s \times 5r$

Statistical diagrams

Exercise 3.1H

1   Draw a pie chart for each of these sets of data.

(a)

Favourite drink	Frequency
Soft drink	42
Milk	12
Water	48
Juice	18
Other	60
Total	180

(b)

Eye colour	Frequency
Blue	76
Blue/Green	28
Brown	92
Grey	38
Other	6
Total	240

(c)

Type of programme	Frequency
Comedy	14
Soap	22
Cartoon	16
Drama	18
Other	10
Total	80

2   Draw a pie chart for each of these sets of data.

(a)

Activity	Hours
School	6
Sleeping	9
Eating	2
Playing	3
TV	2
Other	2

(b)

Favourite TV channel	Frequency
BBC	12
ITV1	15
Channel 4	6
Five	9
Satellite/Cable	30

(c)

Favourite type of film	Frequency
Comedy	25
Horror	14
Romance	32
Action	17
Other	2

Exercise 3.2H

1 The pie chart shows the favourite flavour of crisp
of 60 people questioned in a survey.
How many people preferred
(a) beef flavour?
(b) cheese and onion flavour?
(c) salt and vinegar flavour?

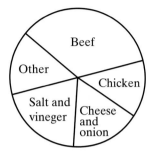

2 The pie chart shows the eye colour of 108 people
questioned in a survey.
How many people had
(a) blue eyes?
(b) grey eyes?

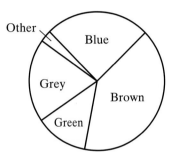

3 The pie charts show the number of companies involved in the automotive trade in the UK in 2006
and 2009.
The total number of companies in each year was the same.

Number of companies in 2006   **Number of companies in 2009**

(a) In which year was the number of car repair companies larger?
(b) What is the main difference between the data for the two years?
(c) What similarities are there between the data for the two years?

Exercise 3.3H

1   For a project, Rebecca recorded the ages of 100 cars as they passed the school gates one morning.
    Here are her results.

Age (*a* years)	$0 \leqslant a < 2$	$2 \leqslant a < 4$	$4 \leqslant a < 6$	$6 \leqslant a < 8$	$8 \leqslant a < 10$	$10 \leqslant a < 12$	$12 \leqslant a < 14$
Frequency	16	23	24	17	12	7	1

(a) Draw a frequency diagram to show these data.
(b) Which of the intervals is the modal group?

2   The manager of a leisure centre recorded the weights of 120 men.
    Here are the results.

Weight (*w* kg)	$60 \leqslant w < 65$	$65 \leqslant w < 70$	$70 \leqslant w < 75$	$75 \leqslant w < 80$	$80 \leqslant w < 85$	$85 \leqslant w < 90$
Frequency	4	18	36	50	10	2

(a) Draw a frequency diagram to represent these data.
(b) Which of the intervals is the modal group?
(c) Which of the intervals contains the median value?

 3   This frequency diagram shows the times taken by a
    group of girls to run a race.
    (a) How many girls took longer than 9 minutes?
    (b) How many girls took part in the race?
    (c) What percentage of the girls took less than 7 minutes?
    (d) What is the modal finishing time?
    (e) Use the diagram to draw up a grouped frequency table
        like those in questions **1** and **2**.

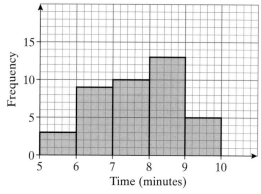

Exercise 3.4H

1   The table shows the heights of 40 plants.

Height (*h* cm)	$3 \leqslant h < 4$	$4 \leqslant h < 5$	$5 \leqslant h < 6$	$6 \leqslant h < 7$	$7 \leqslant h < 8$	$8 \leqslant h < 9$
Frequency	1	7	10	12	8	2

Draw a frequency polygon to show these data.

2   The table shows the time taken for a group of children to get from home to school.

Time (*t* mins)	Frequency
$0 \leqslant t < 5$	3
$5 \leqslant t < 10$	15
$10 \leqslant t < 15$	27
$15 \leqslant t < 20$	34
$20 \leqslant t < 25$	19
$25 \leqslant t < 30$	2

Draw a frequency polygon to show these data.

3   The ages of all of the people under 70 in a small village were recorded in 1990 and 2010.
The results are given in the table below.

Age (*a* years)	Frequency 1990	Frequency 2010
$0 \leqslant a < 10$	85	50
$10 \leqslant a < 20$	78	51
$20 \leqslant a < 30$	70	78
$30 \leqslant a < 40$	53	76
$40 \leqslant a < 50$	40	62
$50 \leqslant a < 60$	28	64
$60 \leqslant a < 70$	18	56

(a) On the same grid, draw a frequency polygon for each year.
(b) Use the diagram to compare the distribution of ages in the two years.

Exercise 3.5H

1   As part of a survey, Emma measured the heights, in centimetres, of the 50 teachers in her school. Here are her results.

168 194 156 167 177 180 188 172 170 169
174 178 186 174 166 165 159 173 185 162
163 174 180 184 173 182 161 176 170 169
178 175 172 179 173 162 177 176 184 191
181 165 163 185 178 175 182 164 179 168

Construct a stem–and–leaf diagram to show these heights.

2   A group of students took a Maths test. Here are their marks.

168 194 156 167 177 180 188 172 170 169
51   94   56   45   70   67   69   49   55   71
52   73   64   60   71   58   64   35   31   81
41   67   64   73   82   57   75   33   88   79
66   52   48

(a) Construct a stem–and–leaf diagram to show these marks.
(b) The pass mark was 40. How many students had to do a re-test?
(c) What is the modal mark?
(d) What is the median mark?

3   The data shows the length of the throws, in metres, in a school shot putt competition.

4.4   5.4   8.5   9.2   7.3   5.7   9.9   9.6   7.4   9.1
7.5   7.0   8.3   4.9   5.7   6.4   6.7   7.3   8.2   9.0
5.2   7.0   8.9   9.1   5.2   6.4   7.3   8.2   5.9   5.0
6.5   7.9   8.2   8.9   5.3   5.2

(a) Construct a stem–and–leaf diagram to show these lengths.
(b) How many people took part in the competition?
(c) Find the median length.

Equations

Exercise 4.1H

Solve these equations.

1 $2x - 3 = 7$　　　　　**2** $2x + 2 = 8$

3 $2x - 9 = 3$　　　　　**4** $3x - 2 = 7$

5 $6x + 2 = 26$　　　　　**6** $3x + 2 = 17$

7 $4x - 5 = 3$　　　　　**8** $4x + 2 = 8$

9 $2x - 7 = 10$　　　　**10** $5x + 12 = 7$

11 $x^2 + 3 = 19$　　　　**12** $x^2 - 2 = 7$

13 $y^2 - 1 = 80$　　　　**14** $11 - 3x = 2$

15 $4x - 12 = -18$

Exercise 4.2H

Solve these equations.

1 $3(x - 2) = 18$　　　　**2** $2(1 + x) = 8$

3 $3(x - 5) = 6$　　　　**4** $2(x + 3) = 10$

5 $5(x - 2) = 15$　　　　**6** $2(x + 3) = 10$

7 $5(x - 4) = 20$　　　　**8** $4(x + 1) = 16$

9 $2(x - 7) = 8$　　　　**10** $3(2x + 3) = 18$

11 $5(2x - 3) = 15$　　　**12** $2(3x - 2) = 14$

13 $5(2x - 3) = 40$　　　**14** $4(x - 3) = 6$

15 $2(2x - 3) = 8$

Exercise 4.3H

Solve these equations.

1 $5x - 1 = 3x + 5$　　　**2** $5x + 1 = 2x + 13$

3 $7x - 2 = 2x + 8$　　　**4** $6x + 1 = 4x + 21$

5 $9x - 10 = 4x + 5$　　　**6** $5x - 8 = 3x - 6$

7 $6x + 2 = 10 - 2x$　　　**8** $2x - 10 = 5 - 3x$

9 $15 + 3x = 2x + 18$　　**10** $2x - 5 = 4 - x$

11 $3x - 2 = x + 7$　　　**12** $x - 1 = 2x - 6$

13 $2x - 4 = 2 - x$　　　**14** $9 - x = x + 5$

15 $3x - 2 = x - 8$　　　**16** $3(2x - 1) = x + 7$

17 $4x + 1 = 2(5 - 3x)$

Exercise 4.4H

Solve these equations.

1 $\frac{x}{2} = 7$　　　　　**2** $\frac{x}{5} - 2 = 1$

3 $\frac{x}{4} + 5 = 8$　　　　**4** $\frac{x}{3} - 5 = 5$

5 $\frac{x}{6} + 3 = 4$　　　　**6** $\frac{x}{5} + 1 = 4$

7 $\frac{x}{8} - 3 = 9$　　　　**8** $\frac{x}{4} + 1 = 3$

9 $\frac{x}{7} + 5 = 6$　　　　**10** $\frac{x}{4} + 5 = 4$

5 Ratio and proportion

Exercise 5.1H

1 Write each of these ratios in its lowest terms.
  (a) 8 : 6
  (b) 20 : 50
  (c) 35 : 55
  (d) 8 : 24 : 32
  (e) 15 : 25 : 20

2 Write each of these ratios in its lowest terms.
  (a) 200 g : 500 g
  (b) 60p : £3
  (c) 1 minute : 25 seconds
  (d) 2 m : 80 cm
  (e) 500 g : 3 kg

3 A bar of brass contains 400 g of copper and 200 g of zinc.
  Write the ratio of copper to zinc in its lowest terms.

4 Teri, Jannae and Abi receive £200, £350 and £450 respectively as their dividends in a joint investment.
  Write the ratio of their dividends in its lowest terms.

5 Three saucepans hold 500 ml, 1 litre and 2.5 litres respectively.
  Write the ratio of their capacities in its lowest terms.

Exercise 5.2H

1 Write each of these ratios in the form 1 : n.
  (a) 2 : 10
  (b) 5 : 30
  (c) 2 : 9
  (d) 4 : 9
  (e) 50 g : 30 g
  (f) 15p : £3
  (g) 25 cm : 6 m
  (h) 20 : 7
  (i) 4 mm : 1 km

2 On a map a distance of 12 mm represents a distance of 3 km.
  What is the scale of the map in the form 1 : n?

3 A picture is enlarged on a photocopier from 25 mm wide to 15 cm wide.
  What is the ratio of the picture to the enlargement in the form 1 : n?

Exercise 5.3H

1 A photo is enlarged in the ratio 1 : 5.
   (a) The length of the small photo is 15 cm.
   What is the length of the large photo?
   (b) The width of the large photo is 45 cm.
   What is the width of the small photo?

2 To make a dressing for her lawn, Rupinder
   mixes loam and sand in the ratio 1 : 3.
   (a) How much sand should she mix with two
   buckets of loam?
   (b) How much loam should she mix with
   15 buckets of sand?

3 To make mortar, Fred mixes 1 part cement with
   5 parts sand.
   (a) How much sand does he mix with 500 g of
   cement?
   (b) How much cement does he mix with 4.5 kg
   of sand?

4 A rectangular picture is 6 cm wide.
   It is enlarged in the ratio 1 : 4.
   How wide is the enlargement?

5 The Michelin motoring atlas of France has a
   scale of 1 cm to 2 km.
   (a) On the map the distance between Metz and
   Nancy is 25 cm.
   How far is the actual distance between the
   two towns?
   (b) The actual distance between Caen and
   Falaise is 33 km.
   How far is this on the map?

6 Graham is making pastry.
   To make enough for five people he uses 300 g
   of flour.
   How much flour should he use for eight people?

7 To make a solution of a chemical a scientist mixes
   2 parts chemical with 25 parts water.
   (a) How much water should he mix with 10 ml
   of chemical?
   (b) How much chemical should he mix with
   1 litre of water?

8 The ratio of the sides of two rectangles is 2 : 5.
   (a) The length of the small rectangle is 4 cm.
   How long is the large rectangle?
   (b) The width of the large rectangle is 7.5 cm.
   How wide is the small rectangle?

9 Jason mixes 3 parts black paint with 4 parts white
   paint to make dark grey paint.
   (a) How much white paint does he mix with
   150 ml of black paint?
   (b) How much black paint does he mix with
   1 litre of white paint?

 10 In an election the number of votes was shared
   between the Labour, Conservatives and other
   parties in the ratio 5 : 4 : 2.
   Labour received 7500 votes.
   (a) How many votes did the Conservatives
   receive?
   (b) How many votes did the other parties
   receive?

Exercise 5.4H

1   Share £40 between Paula and Tariq in the ratio 3 : 5.

2   Paint is mixed in the ratio 2 parts black paint to 3 parts white paint to make 10 litres of grey paint.
    (a) How much black paint is used?
    (b) How much white paint is used?

3   A metal alloy is made up of copper, iron and nickel in the ratio 3 : 4 : 2.
    How much of each metal is there in 450 g of the alloy?

4   Inderjit worked 6 hours one day.
    The time he spent on filing, writing and computing was in the ratio 2 : 3 : 7.
    How long did he spend computing?

5   Daisy and Emily invested £5000 and £8000 respectively in a business venture.
    They agreed to share the profits in the ratio of their investment.
    Emily received £320.
    What was the total profit?

6   Shahida spends her pocket money on sweets, magazines and clothes in the ratio 2 : 3 : 7.
    She receives £15 a week.
    How much does she spend on sweets?

7   In a questionnaire the three possible answers are 'Yes', 'No' and 'Don't know'.
    The answers from a group of 456 people are in the ratio 10 : 6 : 3.
    How many 'Don't knows' are there?

8   Iain and Stephen bought a house between them in Spain.
    Iain paid 60% of the cost and Stephen 40%.
    (a) Write the ratio of the amounts they paid in its lowest terms.
    (b) The house cost 210 000 euros.
        How much did each pay?

Exercise 5.5H

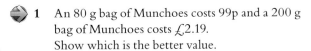

1   An 80 g bag of Munchoes costs 99p and a 200 g bag of Munchoes costs £2.19.
    Show which is the better value.

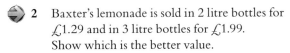

2   Baxter's lemonade is sold in 2 litre bottles for £1.29 and in 3 litre bottles for £1.99.
    Show which is the better value.

3   Butter is sold in 200 g tubs for 95p and in 450 g packets for £2.10.
    Show which is the better value.

4   Fruit yogurt is sold in packs of 4 tubs for 79p and in packs of 12 tubs for £2.19.
    Show which is the better value.

5   There are two packs of minced meat on the reduced price shelf at a supermarket, a 1.8 kg pack reduced to £2.50 and a 1.5 kg pack reduced to £2.
    Show which is the better value.

6   Smoothie shaving gel costs £1.19 for the 75 ml bottle and £2.89 for the 200 ml bottle.
    Show which is better value.

7   A supermarket sells cans of cola in two different sized packs: a pack of 12 cans costs £4.30 and a pack of 20 cans costs £7.25.
    Which pack gives the better value?

8   Sudso washing powder is sold in three sizes: 750 g for £3.15, 1.5 kg for £5.99 and 2.5 kg for £6.99.
    Which size gives the best value?

Chapter 6 — Statistical calculations

Exercise 6.1H

1   For each of these sets of data
    (i)   find the mode.
    (ii) find the median.
    (iii) find the range.
    (iv) calculate the mean.

(a)

Score on biased dice	Number of times thrown
1	52
2	46
3	70
4	54
5	36
6	42
Total	300

(b)

Number of drawing pins in a box	Number of boxes
98	5
99	14
100	36
101	28
102	17
103	13
104	7
Total	120

(c)

Number of snacks per day	Frequency
0	23
1	68
2	39
3	21
4	10
5	3
6	1

(d)

Number of letters received on Monday	Frequency
0	19
1	37
2	18
3	24
4	12
5	5
6	2
7	3

2   Gift tokens cost £1, £5, £10, £20 or £50 each.
    The frequency table shows the numbers of each
    value of gift token sold in one bookstore on a
    Saturday.

Price of gift token (£)	Number of tokens sold
1	12
5	34
10	26
20	9
50	1

Calculate the mean value of gift token bought in
the bookstore that Saturday.

3   A sample of people were asked how many visits
    to the cinema they had made in one month.
    None of those asked had made more than eight
    visits to the cinema.
    The table shows the data.

Number of visits	Frequency
0	136
1	123
2	72
3	41
4	18
5	0
6	5
7	1
8	4

Calculate the mean number of visits to the
cinema.

Exercise 6.2H

1   For each of these sets of data, calculate an
    estimate of
    (i) the range.
    (ii) the mean.

(a)

Number of trains arriving late each day (x)	Number of days (f)
0–4	19
5–9	9
10–14	3
15–19	0
20–24	1
Total	32

(b)

Number of weeds per square metre (x)	Number of square metres (f)
0–14	204
15–29	101
30–44	39
45–59	13
60–74	6
75–89	2

(c)

Number of books sold (x)	Frequency (f)
60–64	3
65–69	12
70–74	23
75–79	9
80–84	4
85–89	1

(d)

Number of days absent (x)	Frequency (f)
0–3	13
4–7	18
8–11	9
12–15	4
16–19	0
20–23	1
24–27	3

2   The table gives the number of sentences per chapter in a book.

Number of sentences (x)	Frequency
$100 \leqslant x < 125$	1
$125 \leqslant x < 150$	9
$150 \leqslant x < 175$	8
$175 \leqslant x < 200$	5
$200 \leqslant x < 225$	2

(a) What is the modal class?
(b) In which class is the median number of sentences?
(c) Calculate an estimate of the mean number of sentences.

3   A group of students were asked to estimate the number of beans in a jar.
The results of their estimates are summarised in the table.

Estimated number of beans (x)	Frequency (f)
300–324	9
325–349	26
350–374	52
375–399	64
400–424	83
425–449	57
450–474	18
475–499	5

Calculate an estimate of the mean number of beans estimated by these students.

Exercise 6.3H

1   For each of these sets of data, calculate an estimate of
(i) the range.
(ii) the mean.

(a)

Height of sunflower in centimetres (x)	Number of plants (f)
$100 \leqslant x < 110$	6
$110 \leqslant x < 120$	13
$120 \leqslant x < 130$	35
$130 \leqslant x < 140$	29
$140 \leqslant x < 150$	16
$150 \leqslant x < 160$	11
Total	110

(b)

Weight of egg in grams (x)	Number of eggs (f)
$20 \leqslant x < 25$	9
$25 \leqslant x < 30$	16
$30 \leqslant x < 35$	33
$35 \leqslant x < 40$	48
$40 \leqslant x < 45$	29
$45 \leqslant x < 50$	15
Total	150

(c)

Length of green bean in millimetres (x)	Frequency (f)
$60 \leqslant x < 80$	12
$80 \leqslant x < 100$	21
$100 \leqslant x < 120$	46
$120 \leqslant x < 140$	27
$140 \leqslant x < 160$	14
Total	120

(d)

Time to complete race in minutes (x)	Frequency (f)
$54 \leqslant x < 56$	1
$56 \leqslant x < 58$	4
$58 \leqslant x < 60$	11
$60 \leqslant x < 62$	6
$62 \leqslant x < 64$	2
$64 \leqslant x < 66$	1
Total	25

2 For each of these sets of data
  (i) write down the modal class.
  (ii) calculate an estimate of the mean.

(a)

Height of shrub in metres (x)	Number of shrubs (f)
$0.3 \leqslant x < 0.6$	57
$0.6 \leqslant x < 0.9$	41
$0.9 \leqslant x < 1.2$	36
$1.2 \leqslant x < 1.5$	24
$1.5 \leqslant x < 1.8$	15

(b)

Weight of plum in grams (x)	Number of plums (f)
$20 \leqslant x < 30$	6
$30 \leqslant x < 40$	19
$40 \leqslant x < 50$	58
$50 \leqslant x < 60$	15
$60 \leqslant x < 70$	4

(c)

Length of journey in minutes (x)	Frequency (f)
$20 \leqslant x < 22$	6
$22 \leqslant x < 24$	20
$24 \leqslant x < 26$	38
$26 \leqslant x < 28$	47
$28 \leqslant x < 30$	16
$30 \leqslant x < 32$	3

(d)

Speed of car in miles per hour (x)	Frequency (f)
25 ≤ x < 30	4
30 ≤ x < 35	29
35 ≤ x < 40	33
40 ≤ x < 45	6
45 ≤ x < 50	2
50 ≤ x < 55	1

3 The table shows the monthly wages of the workers in an office.

Wages in £ (x)	Frequency (f)
500 ≤ x < 1000	3
1000 ≤ x < 1500	14
1500 ≤ x < 2000	18
2000 ≤ x < 2500	5

(a) What is the modal class?
(b) In which class is the median wage?
(c) Calculate an estimate of the mean wage.

4 The table shows the length, in seconds, of 100 calls made from a mobile phone.

Length of call in seconds (x)	Frequency (f)
0 ≤ x < 30	51
30 ≤ x < 60	25
60 ≤ x < 90	13
90 ≤ x < 120	7
120 ≤ x < 150	4

Calculate an estimate of the mean length of a call.

5 The table shows the prices paid for greetings cards sold in one day by a card shop.

Price of greetings card in pence (x)	Frequency (f)
75 ≤ x < 100	23
100 ≤ x < 125	31
125 ≤ x < 150	72
150 ≤ x < 175	59
175 ≤ x < 200	34
200 ≤ x < 225	11
225 ≤ x < 250	5

Calculate an estimate of the mean price, in pence, paid for a greetings card that day.

Pythagoras' theorem

Exercise 7.1H

For each of these diagrams, find the area of the third square.

1

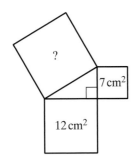

2

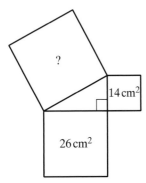

3

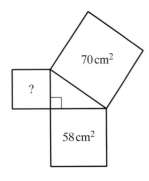

4

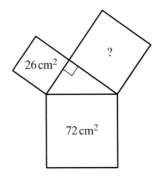

Exercise 7.2H

1 For each of these triangles, find the length marked x.
Where the answer is not exact, give your answer correct to 2 decimal places.

(a)

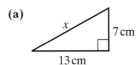

(b)

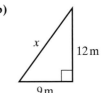

(c)

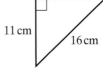

(d)

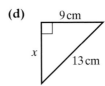

(e)

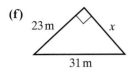

(f)

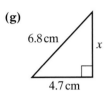

(g)

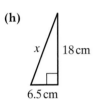

(h)

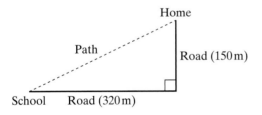

2 Ann can walk home from school along two roads or along a path across a field.

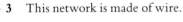
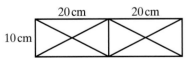

How much shorter is her journey if she takes the path across the field?

3 This network is made of wire.

What is the total length of wire?

Exercise 7.3H

Work out whether or not each of these triangles is right-angled.
Show your working.

1

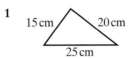

2

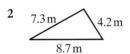

3

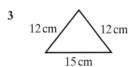

4

5

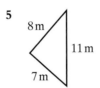

6

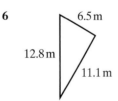

7

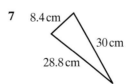

8

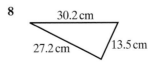

Exercise 7.4H

1   Calculate the length of the diagonal of a cuboid measuring 6 cm by 10 cm by 5 cm.

 2   The length of the diagonal of a cube is 6.8 cm. Find the length of a side of this cube.

3   In this cuboid, AB = 10 cm, BC = 6 cm and CG = 8 cm.

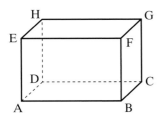

Calculate
(a) the length of EG.
(b) the length of HB.

Exercise 7.5H

1   For each of the line segments in the diagram
(i) find the coordinates of the midpoint.
(ii) find the length. Where the answer is not exact, give your answer to 2 decimal places.

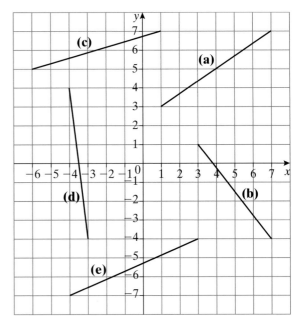

2   For the line segments joining each of these pairs of points
(a) A(2, 7) and B(6, 4)
(b) C(5, 8) and D(7, 2)
(c) E(3, 8) and F(7, −1)
(d) G(6, 5) and H(−6, 0)
(e) I(−3, 2) and J(−8, −5)
(f) K(−7, 2) and L(3, 6)

(i) find the coordinates of the midpoint.
(ii) find the length. Where the answer is not exact, give your answer to 2 decimal places.

Chapter

8

Formulae 1

Exercise 8.1H

1   Pearl is a child minder.
    She charges £6.50 an hour.
    She looks after Mrs Khan's child for 6 hours.
    How much does she charge?

2   It costs £60 plus £1 a mile to hire a coach.
    (a) How much does it cost to hire a coach to go
        (i) 80 miles?   **(ii)** 150 miles?
    (b) Write a formula for the cost, £C, of hiring a
        coach to go n miles.

3   The cost of booking a room for a meeting is £80
    plus £20 an hour.
    (a) How much does it cost to hire the room for
        (i) 5 hours?   **(ii)** 8 hours?
    (b) Write a formula for the cost, £C, of hiring
        the room for h hours.

4   The perimeter of a rectangle is twice the length
    plus twice the width.
    (a) What is the perimeter of a rectangle with
        length 5 cm and width 3.5 cm?
    (b) Write a formula for the perimeter, P, of a
        rectangle with length x and width y.

5   To find the volume of a pyramid, multiply the
    area of the base by the height and divide by 3.
    (a) What is the volume of a pyramid with a base
        of area 12 cm^2 and a height of 7 cm?
    (b) Write a formula for the volume, V, of a
        pyramid with a base of area A and a height
        of h.

6   To find the time it takes to type a document,
    divide the number of words in the document by
    the number of words typed per minute.
    (a) How long does it take Liz to type a
        document 560 words long if she types
        80 words a minute?
    (b) Write a formula for the time, T, to type a
        document w words long if the typist types
        r words a minute.

7   The time, t, for a journey is the distance, d,
    divided by the speed, s.
    (a) Write a formula for this.
    (b) Steve travelled 175 miles at a speed of
        50 mph.
        How long did the journey take?

8   The circumference of a circle is given by the
    formula $C = \pi \times D$, where D is the diameter of
    the circle.
    Find the circumference of a circle with a
    diameter of 8.5 cm. Use $\pi = 3.14$.

9   At Carterknowle toddlers group the charge is £1
    per carer and 50p for every toddler they bring.
    (a) Tracey brings three toddlers to the group.
        How much does she pay?
    (b) Fran brings n toddlers to the group.
        Write down a formula for the amount, £A,
        she has to pay.

10 **(a)** For the formula $A = b - c$, find A when
        $b = 6$ and $c = 3.5$.
    (b) For the formula $B = 2a - b$, find B when
        $a = 6$ and $b = 5$.
    (c) For the formula $C = 2a - b - 3c$, find C when
        $a = 3.5$, $b = 2.6$ and $c = 1.2$.
    (d) For the formula $D = 3b^2$, find D when
        $b = 2$.
    (e) For the formula $E = ab - cd$, find E when
        $a = 12.5$, $b = 6$, $c = 3.5$ and $d = 8$.
    (f) For the formula $F = \dfrac{a - b}{5}$, find F when
        $a = 6$ and $b = 3.5$.

11 A cardboard square has sides of length $3x$ cm.
    A square hole with sides of length x cm is cut out
    of the cardboard square.
    (a) Write an expression for the area of the
        remaining cardboard.
    (b) Find the area of remaining cardboard if the
        sides of the hole are 2 cm.

Exercise 8.2H

1 Rearrange each of these formulae to make the letter in brackets the subject.

(a) $a = b + c$ (b)

(b) $a = 3x - y$ (x)

(c) $a = b + ct$ (t)

(d) $F = 2(q + p)$ (q)

(e) $x = 2y - 3z$ (y)

(f) $P = \dfrac{3 + 4n}{5}$ (n)

2 The formula for the circumference of a circle is
$C = \pi d$.
Rearrange the formula to make d the subject.

3 Rearrange the formula $A = \dfrac{3ab}{2n}$ to make

(a) a the subject.

(b) n the subject.

4 The formula for finding the perimeter of a rectangle is $P = 2(a + b)$, where P is the perimeter, a is the length and b is the width of the rectangle.
Rearrange the formula to make a the subject.

5 The formula $y = mx + c$ is the equation of a straight line.
Rearrange it to find m in terms of x, y and c.

6 The surface area of a sphere is given by the formula $A = 4\pi r^2$.
Rearrange the formula to make r the subject.

7 The formula for the volume of this prism is
$V = \dfrac{\pi r^2 h}{4}$.

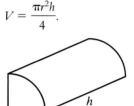

(a) Find V when $r = 2.5$ and $h = 7$.

(b) (i) Rearrange the formula to make r the subject.

     (ii) Find r when $V = 100$ and $h = 10$.

8 The formula for the surface area of a closed cylinder is $S = 2\pi r(r + h)$.
Rearrange the formula to make h the subject.

9 Measures

Exercise 9.1H

1 Change these lengths to centimetres.
   (a) 2 m   (b) 3.5 m   (c) 20 mm
   (d) 15 m   (e) 45 mm

2 Change these lengths to millimetres.
   (a) 2 cm   (b) 5.5 cm   (c) 10 cm
   (d) 2 m   (e) 3.5 m

3 Change these weights to grams.
   (a) 2 kg   (b) 5 kg   (c) 6.35 kg
   (d) 0.8 kg   (e) 0.525 kg

4 Put these volumes in order, smallest first.
   1.2 litres   500 ml   2 litres
   2500 ml   800 cl

5 Which metric units would you use to measure these lengths?
   (a) The span of your hand
   (b) The length of a corridor
   (c) The width of a window
   (d) The distance you can walk in a day
   (e) The distance from London to Edinburgh

6 Put these weights in order, smallest first.
   1.2 kg   1500 g   160 g
   2000 g   0.8 kg

7 Change these volumes to millilitres.
   (a) 2 litres   (b) 3.5 litres   (c) 2 cl
   (d) 15 cl   (e) 0.345 litres

8 Graham has three pieces of string.
   The lengths are 45 cm, 85 mm and 1.2 m.
   (a) Write them down in order, shortest first.
   (b) What is the total length of string
       (i)   in millimetres?
       (ii) in centimetres?
       (iii) in metres?

Exercise 9.2H

Here are some approximate conversions between imperial and metric units.

Length	Mass
8 km ≈ 5 miles	1 kg ≈ 2 pounds (lb)
1 m ≈ 40 inches	**Capacity**
1 inch ≈ 2.5 cm	4 litres ≈ 7 pints (pt)
1 foot (ft) ≈ 30 cm	9 litres ≈ 2 gallons

1 Change these measures from imperial units to their approximate metric units.
   (a) 6 feet   (b) 35 miles   (c) 14 lb
   (d) 45 lb   (e) 14 pints

2 Change these measures from metric units to their approximate imperial units.
   (a) 24 km   (b) 5 m   (c) 5 kg
   (d) 12 litres   (e) 20 cm

3 Stephen needs 1 pound of meat for a recipe. How many grams should he buy?

4 A radiator is 20 inches wide. What is this in centimetres?

5 Cola is sold in 2 litre bottles. How much is this in pints?

6 Pauline is 5 foot 4 inches tall. What is this in centimetres?

7 A more accurate conversion between kilograms and pounds is 1 kg ≈ 2.2 lbs.
   Sarfraz weighs 45 kg.
   (a) What is this in pounds?
   Many people still talk about how much they weight in stones and pounds.
   There are 14 pounds in a stone.
   (b) What does Sarfraz weigh in stones and pounds?

8 Mark drives towards Nottingham and sees this sign.

| Grantham | 23 miles |
| Nottingham | 53 miles |

Roughly how far is it, in kilometres, from Grantham to Nottingham?

Exercise 9.3H

1 Estimate the following.
  (a) The height your desk
  (b) The width of a door
  (c) The mass of a glass of water
  (d) The capacity of a kitchen sink
  (e) The distance you can walk in an hour

2 Estimate the height of this lamp post.

3 The building in this picture is about 16 m high. Estimate the height of the lorry.

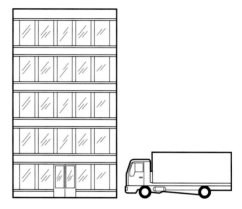

4 Alan wants to estimate the length of his bedroom.
His foot is 20 cm long.
He works out that the room is 16 foot lengths long.
What is his estimate of the length of his bedroom?

5 Adrian is asked to estimate the distance he walks to school.
His answer is 1.135 km.
  (a) Why is this not a sensible estimate?
  (b) What would be a better estimate?

Chapter 10 | Planning and collecting

Exercise 10.1H

1 State whether the following would produce primary data or secondary data.
  (a) Weighing packets of sweets
  (b) Using bus timetables
  (c) Looking up holiday prices on the internet
  (d) A GP entering data for a new patient on her records after seeing the patient

2 Lisa is doing a survey and has written this question.

> **What colour is your hair?**
>
> Black ☐   Brown ☐   Blonde ☐

  (a) Give a reason why this question is unsuitable.
  (b) Write a better version.

3 Steve is doing a survey about his local sports facilities.
Here is one of his questions.

> **How much do you enjoy doing sport?**
>
>   1   2   3   4   5

  (a) Give a reason why this question is unsuitable.
  (b) Write a better version.

4 Mia is doing a survey about school lunches. She gives out questionnaires to the first 30 people in the queue for lunch.
  (a) Why is this likely to give a biased sample?
  (b) Describe a better method of obtaining a sample for her survey.

5 Here is one of Mia's questions.

> **Don't you agree that we don't have enough salads on the menu?**

  (a) Give a reason why this question is unsuitable.
  (b) Write a better version.

6 A survey is to be done about school students' earnings and pocket money.
Write five suitable questions which could be included in such a survey.

Sequences

Exercise 11.1H

1 Look at this sequence of patterns.
The first four patterns in the sequence have been drawn.

   (a) How many circles are there in the 100th pattern?
   (b) Describe the position-to-term rule for this sequence.

2 Look at this sequence of matchstick patterns.

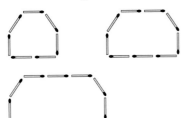

   (a) Copy and complete this table.

Pattern number	Number of matchsticks
1	
2	
3	
4	
5	

   (b) What patterns can you see in the numbers?
   (c) Find the number of matchsticks in the 50th pattern.

3 Here is a sequence of star patterns.

```
                              *   *   *
                  *   *       *   *   *
        *         *   *       *   *   *
        *         *   *       *   *   *
```

   (a) Draw the next pattern in the sequence.
   (b) Without drawing the pattern, find the number of stars in the 8th pattern.
      Explain how you found your answer.

4 The numbers in a sequence are given by this rule:
      Multiply the position number by 7, then subtract 10.
   (a) Show that the first term of the sequence is −3.
   (b) Find the next four terms in the sequence.

5 Find the first four terms of the sequences with these nth terms.
   (a) $10n$ **(b)** $8n + 2$

6 Find the first five terms of the sequences with these nth terms.
   (a) n^2 **(b)** $2n^2$ **(c)** $5n^2$

7 The first term of a sequence is 3.
   The general rule for the sequence is multiply a term by 3 to get to the next term.
   Write down the first five terms of the sequence.

8 For a sequence, $T_1 = 12$ and $T_{n+1} = T_n - 5$.
   Write down the first four terms of this sequence.

9 Draw suitable patterns to represent this sequence.
      1, 4, 7, 10, ...

10 Draw suitable patterns to represent this sequence.
      $1 \times 1, 3 \times 3, 5 \times 5, 7 \times 7, ...$

Exercise 11.2H

1 Find the nth term for each of these sequences.
  (a) 10, 13, 16, 19, 22, ...
  (b) 0, 1, 2, 3, 4, ...
  (c) −3, −1, 1, 3, 5, ...

2 Find the nth term for each of these sequences.
  (a) 25, 20, 15, 10, 5, ...
  (b) 4, 2, 0, −2, −4, ...
  (c) 3, 2, 1, 0, −1, ...

3 Which of these sequences are linear?
  Find the next two terms of each of the sequences that are linear.
  (a) 2, 5, 10, 17, ...
  (b) 2, 5, 8, 11, ...
  (c) 1, 3, 6, 10, ...
  (d) 12, 8, 4, 0, −4, ...

 4 **(a)** Write the first five terms of the sequence with nth term $100n$.
  (b) Compare your answers with this sequence.

    99, 199, 299, 399, ...

  Write down the nth term of this sequence.

5 A mail-order shirt company charges £25 per shirt, plus an overall delivery charge of £3.
  (a) Copy and complete this table.

Number of shirts	Cost in £
1	
2	
3	

  (b) Write an expression for the cost, in pounds, of n shirts.
  (c) Paul pays £128 for shirts. How many does he buy?

6 **(a)** Write down the first five terms of the sequence with nth term n^2.
  (b) Compare your answers with this sequence.

    0, 3, 8, 15, 24, ...

  Write the nth term of this sequence.

7 The nth triangular number is $\dfrac{n(n+1)}{2}$.
  Find the 60th triangular number.

8 The nth term of a sequence is 2^n.
  (a) Write down the first five terms of this sequence.
  (b) Describe the sequence.

 9 **(a)** Write down the first five cube numbers.
  (b) Compare this sequence with the sequence of cube numbers.

    3, 10, 29, 66, 127, ...

  Use what you notice to write down the nth term of this sequence.
  (c) Find the 10th term of this sequence.

 10 **(a)** Compare this sequence with the sequence of square numbers.

    5, 20, 45, 80, 125, ...

  Use what you notice to write down the nth term of this sequence.
  (b) Find the 20th term of this sequence.

Chapter 12 | Constructions and loci

Exercise 12.1H

1 Two points, A and B, are 7 cm apart.
Construct the locus of points that are equidistant from A and B.

2 A badger will never go further than 3 miles from its home.
Construct a scale diagram to show the regions where the badger might go looking for food.

 3 Draw an equilateral triangle, ABC, of side 6 cm.
Shade the region of points inside the triangle which are nearer to AB than to AC.

4 A rectangular garden measures 8 m by 6 m.
A fence is built from F, at a right angle across the garden.

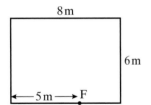

Draw a scale diagram and construct the line of the fence.

5 Draw a square, ABCD, of side 5 cm.
Construct the locus of points, inside the square, which are more than 3 cm from A.

6 Zeke is walking across a field.
He notices a bull starting to chase him.
He runs the shortest distance to the hedge.
Copy the diagram and construct the path that Zeke should run.

• Zeke

7 Draw a rectangle, PQRS, with sides PQ = 7 cm and QR = 5 cm.
Shade the region of points within PQRS that are closer to P than to Q.

8 Draw an angle of 80°.
Construct the bisector of the angle.

 9 An office is a rectangle measuring 16 m by 12 m.
There are two electricity points in the office at opposite corners of the room.
The vacuum cleaner has a wire 10 m long.
Make a scale drawing to show how much of the room can be cleaned.

 10 Make another scale drawing of the office in question **9**.
Shade the locus of points which are equidistant from the two electricity points.
Use this locus to work out the length of wire needed for the vacuum cleaner to reach everywhere in the office.

Exercise 12.2H

 1 Draw a point and label it P.
Construct the locus of points that are less than 4 cm from P or more than 6 cm from P.

2 A rectangular garden measures 20 m by 12 m.
A tree is to be planted so that it is more than 4 m from each corner of the garden.
Make a scale drawing to find the area where the tree can be planted.

 3 Two points, A and B, are 5 cm apart.
Find the region that is less than 3 cm from A and more than 4 cm from B.

 4 Make an accurate drawing of a triangle, PQR, where PQ = 6 cm, P = 40° and Q = 35°.
Find the point X, which is 2 cm from R and equidistant from P and Q.

5 Two coastguard stations, A and B, are 20 km apart on a straight coastline.
The coastguard at A knows that a ship is within 15 km of him.
The coastguard at B knows that the same ship is within 10 km of him.
Make a scale drawing to show the region where the ship could be.

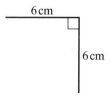

 6 Two lines, each 6 cm long, join to form a right angle.
Draw the region of points which are less than 3 cm from these lines.

 7 Two points, P and Q, are 7 cm apart.
Find the points which are the same distance from P and Q and are also within 5 cm of Q.

 8 The diagram shows three coastguard stations, C, D and E.
A ship is within 25 km of C and closer to DE than DC.
Find the region where the ship could be.

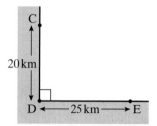

 9 A garden is a rectangle, ABCD, with AB = 5 m and BC = 3 m.
A new flower bed is to be made in the garden.
It must be more than 2 m from A and less than 1.5 m from CD.
Make a scale drawing to show where the flower bed could be.

 10 EFG is a triangle with EF = 6 cm, FG = 8 cm and EG = 10 cm.
Construct the perpendicular from F to EG.
Indicate the points on this line that are more than 7 cm from G.

Chapter 13 | Sampling

Exercise 13.1H

1 A call centre records the calls its operators make. The table shows the duration of the calls recorded one day.

Duration (minutes)	Number of calls
0 to 1	230
1 to 2	420
2 to 3	480
3 and over	358

50 calls are to be selected at random, to be reviewed by the centre manager.
How many calls should be selected from each band to make the sample representative?

2 A simple random sample of 20 households in a particular street of a town are to be surveyed about their refuse collection. The houses in the street are numbered 1 to 60.

Use the random number table below to choose the sample. Start at the top left corner and work your way along the first and subsequent rows, examining pairs of digits in the table. Write down the first 20 pairs which lie between 01 and 60, ignoring repetitions and those values outside the range.

980677	461663	998081	821548	961256
402566	215166	163433	183641	331870
685871	249206	948448	929632	290060
783289	766103	012094	363987	522723

3 A systematic random sample of 20 households in the same street as in question **2** are to be surveyed about how often they travel by bus.

Since 20 out of 60 is the same as 1 in 3, you need to randomly select a starting value between 1 and 3. Starting at the beginning of row 2 of the random number table, look at single digits and find the first value which lies between 1 and 3. Use this as the start of your systematic sample.

Write down the 20 house numbers that this method gives.

4 The students of a school are to be surveyed about a new school uniform.
100 students are to be interviewed.
The table shows the number of students in each year group.

Year	7	8	9	10	11
Number of students	142	154	115	127	102

How many students from each year group should be selected to provide a representative sample?

Exercise 13.2H

In each of these questions, decide whether or not the method of sampling is appropriate. If it is not satisfactory, say why not.

1 A candidate in a local election wishes to establish how people are likely to vote. He decides to telephone every 50th person in the telephone directory.

2 To obtain information about diseases amongst the elderly, everyone in a large residential home is given a thorough health check.

3 The Post Office is interested to know how people feel about proposed changes to delivery times for letters. They send a letter to every household and ask their views.

4 A manufacturer is about to introduce a new flavour of crisps. They stop people in the street and offer them some of the crisps to taste.

5 To find people's views about an increase in income tax, a random sample of ten people are stopped and questioned in the street one morning.

Trigonometry

Exercise 14.1H

1 In these diagrams find the lengths marked *a*, *b*, *c*, *d*, *e*, *f*, *g* and *h*.

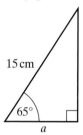

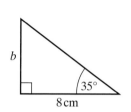

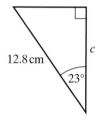

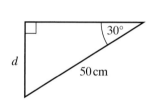

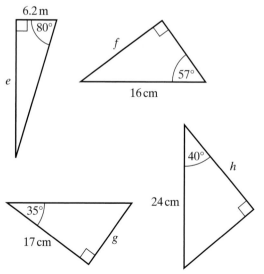

2 The diagram shows the side view of a waste bin.

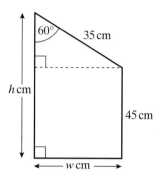

(a) Find the width, *w* cm, of the bin.
(b) Find the height, *h* cm, of the bin.

3 The diagram shows a triangle.

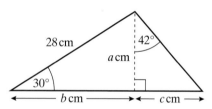

(a) Find the height, *a* cm, of the triangle.
(b) Find the length, *b* cm.
(c) Find the length, *c* cm.
(d) Use your answers to parts (a), (b) and (c) to find the area of the triangle.

 4 An isosceles triangle has two equal sides of 8 cm and a base of *x* cm.
The angle between the two equal sides is 36°.
(a) Find the perpendicular height of the triangle.
Give your answer to 1 decimal place.
(b) Find the value of *x* to 1 decimal place.
(c) Find the area of the triangle to 1 decimal place.

Exercise 14.2H

1 In these diagrams find the lengths marked *a*, *b*, *c*, *d*, *e*, *f*, *g* and *h*.

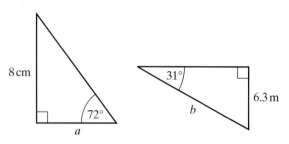

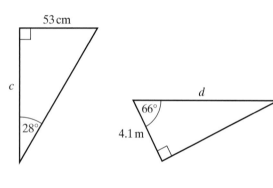

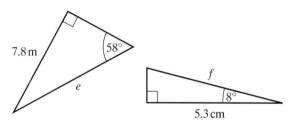

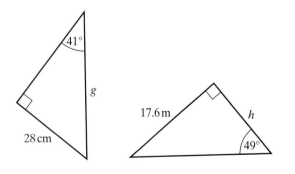

2 The diagram shows a step ladder.
The two sections of the ladder are opened to 30°.
The feet of the two parts are 1.2 m apart.

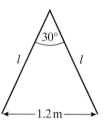

Calculate the length, *l*, of each section of the ladder.

3 The diagram shows a triangle.

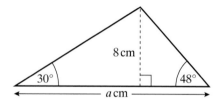

(a) Find the base, *a* cm, of the triangle.
(b) Use the base you found in part **(a)** to find the area of the triangle.

4 A man wants to lay a straight path along the diagonal of his rectangular garden.
The garden is 24 m long and the diagonal makes an angle of 66° with one of the sides of the garden.
(a) Find the width of the garden.
(b) Find the length of the path.
(c) The man has 50 half-metre square paving stones.
Does he have enough to complete the path?
If not, how many more paving stones would he need to buy?

Exercise 14.3H

1 In these diagrams find the angles marked a, b, c, d, e, f, g and h.

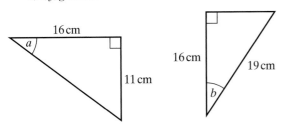

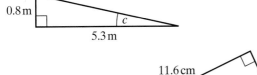

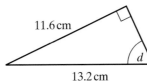

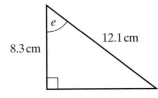

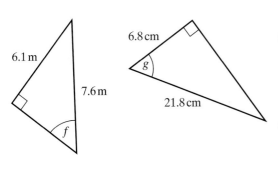

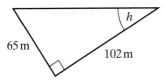

2 A rectangle has a length of 12 cm and a width of 8 cm.
Calculate the angle the diagonal makes with the longest side.

3 A yacht sails from A to B.
B is 43 km east of A and 25 km south of A.

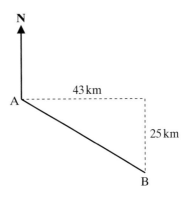

Calculate the bearing of B from A.

4 The diagram shows an isosceles triangle.

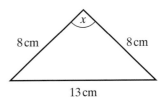

Calculate the size of angle x.

5 A boat is sailing at a point 160 m away from a cliff.
The cliff is 76 m high.
Find the angle of elevation from the boat to the top of the cliff.

6 A girl is taking her dog for a walk on a lead.
The lead is 1.7 m long and the dog is walking 1.5 m ahead of the girl.
Find the angle the lead makes with the horizontal.

Exercise 15.1H

1   This cumulative frequency graph shows the heights of 80 sunflowers.
    Find the median, the quartiles and the interquartile range of these heights.

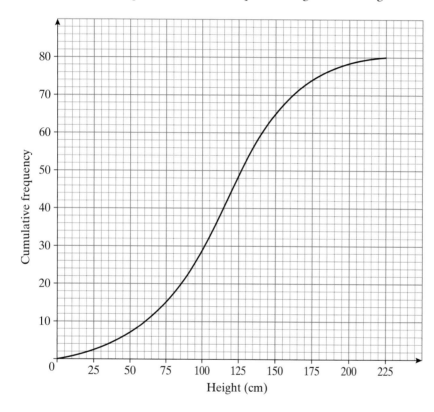

2 The table on the left shows information about the masses of 140 tomatoes.

(a) Copy and complete the cumulative frequency table on the right.

Mass (m grams)	Frequency
$0 < m \leqslant 20$	4
$20 < m \leqslant 40$	14
$40 < m \leqslant 60$	25
$60 < m \leqslant 80$	47
$80 < m \leqslant 100$	36
$100 < m \leqslant 120$	14

Mass (m grams)	Cumulative frequency
$m \leqslant 0$	0
$m \leqslant 20$	4
$m \leqslant 40$	18
$m \leqslant 60$	
$m \leqslant 80$	
$m \leqslant 100$	
$m \leqslant 120$	

(b) Draw the cumulative frequency graph.

(c) Use your graph to find the median and interquartile range of these masses.

3 The table on the left shows the ages of people in a health club.

(a) Copy and complete the cumulative frequency table on the right.
    Note: the upper boundary of the 11–18 age group is the 19th birthday.

Age (years)	Frequency
under 11	32
11–18	25
19–29	53
30–49	83
50–69	45
70–94	21

Age (years)	Cumulative Frequency
$y < 0$	0
$y < 11$	32
$y < 19$	57
$y < 30$	110
$y <$	
$y <$	
$y <$	

(b) Draw the cumulative frequency graph.

(c) How many people in this club are aged under 40?

(d) How many people in this club are aged 60 or over?

(e) Find the median and the quartiles.

4 The cumulative frequency graph shows the foot lengths of a sample of 50 boys and 50 girls.

(a) What does the flat section at the top of the girls' graph tell you?

(b) Compare the distributions. Make two comparisons.

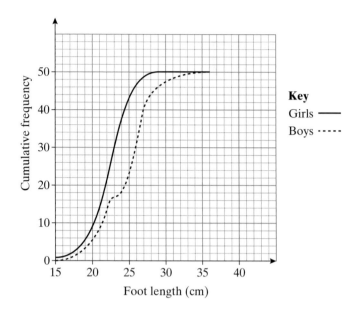

Key
Girls ——
Boys - - - - -

5 The stem-and-leaf diagram represents the marks gained by 35 students in a test.

```
3 | 2  5
4 | 2  3  6  8
5 | 0  1  2  3  7
6 | 1  2  4  4  7  8  8
7 | 0  0  1  2  3  4  5  6  7  9
8 | 1  3  4  6  7
9 | 3  5
```

Key: 4 | 8 represents 48 marks.
Copy and complete this table for the distribution.

Minimum (Q_0)	LQ (Q_1)	Median (Q_2)	UQ (Q_3)	Maximum (Q_4)

6 This table shows the distance walked by each of a group of students one day.
Draw a cumulative frequency graph and a box plot to represent this distribution.

Distance (d miles)	Frequency
$0 < d \leqslant 2$	4
$2 < d \leqslant 4$	16
$4 < d \leqslant 6$	8
$6 < d \leqslant 8$	6
$8 < d \leqslant 10$	2

7   Here is a summary for a distribution of marks gained by a year group in an examination.

Minimum (Q₀)	LQ (Q₁)	Median (Q₂)	UQ (Q₃)	Maximum (Q₄)
27	45	62	74	93

Draw a box plot for this distribution.

8   The cumulative frequency graph represents the distances swum by children in a sponsored swim.

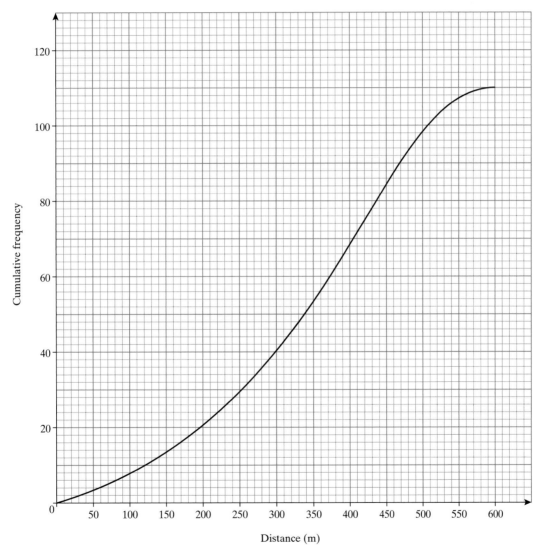

(a) How many children took part in the swim?
(b) How many children swam over 400 m?
(c) Draw a box plot for this distribution.

9 These box plots represent the time, in hours, spent watching TV by samples of 50 boys and 50 girls one week. Make two comparisons between the times spent by the boys and the girls, stating which statistics you use.

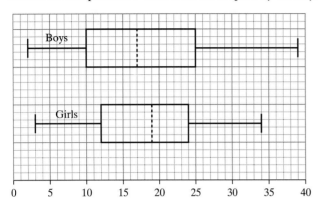

10 A company tested a sample of 200 torch batteries of each of two types it produces. The table summarises the results, showing the time, in hours, that each battery lasted.

Time (t hours)	Frequency for type A	Frequency for type B
$0 < t \leqslant 5$	4	12
$5 < t \leqslant 10$	31	61
$10 < t \leqslant 15$	45	71
$15 < t \leqslant 20$	87	32
$20 < t \leqslant 25$	27	16
$25 < t \leqslant 30$	6	8

(a) On the same axes, draw cumulative frequency graphs to represent these distributions. Below your graphs, draw box plots for the distributions.

(b) Which of the two types of battery is more reliable?

Exercise 15.2H

1 The table shows the amounts spent at the supermarket by a sample of people.
Draw a histogram to represent this distribution.
Label your vertical scale or key clearly.

Amount spent (£s)	Frequency
$0 \leqslant s < 20$	12
$20 \leqslant s < 40$	16
$40 \leqslant s < 70$	33
$70 \leqslant s < 100$	12
$100 \leqslant s < 150$	6

2 This distribution shows the ages of people visiting a swimming pool one day.
   (a) Explain why the boundary of the 30–49 group is 50 years.
   (b) Calculate the frequency densities and draw a histogram to represent this distribution.

Age (years)	Frequency
Under 10	96
10–19	58
20–29	36
30–49	58
50–89	144

3 The histogram represents a distribution of waiting times for non-emergency operations at a particular hospital.

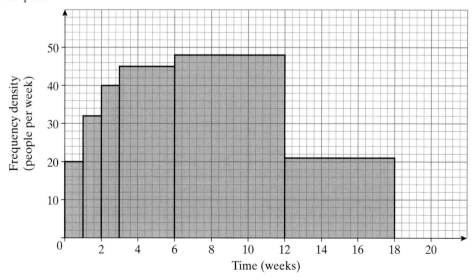

   (a) Make a frequency table for this distribution.
   (b) Calculate an estimate of the mean waiting time.

4 The histograms represent the times spent on a project by a sample of girls and boys.

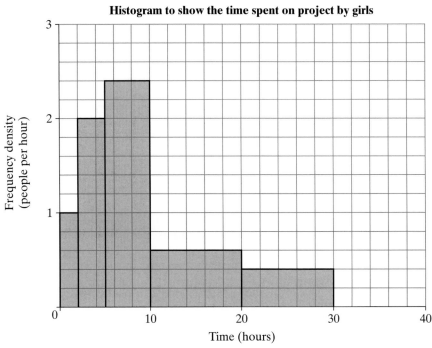

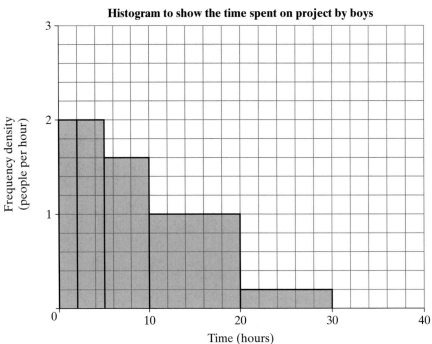

(a) Find how many girls and how many boys spent between 5 and 10 hours on the project.
(b) Compare the distributions.

5 The members of a gym were measured. The histogram represents their heights.

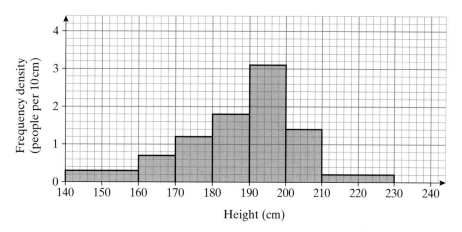

(a) How many members of the gym were measured?
(b) Calculate an estimate of their mean height.
(c) Find an estimate of the median height of the members.

Exercise 15.3H

1 This cumulative frequency diagram shows the lifetimes of two types of lightbulb, A and B.

Compare the performances of the two types of lightbulb using the median and the interquartile range.

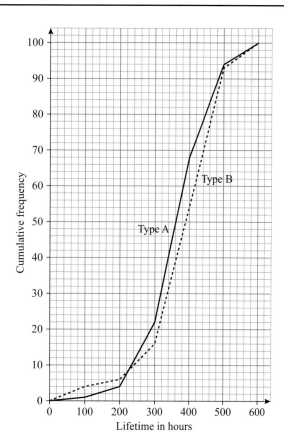

Exercise 16.1H

Rearrange each of these formulae to make the letter in brackets the subject.

1   $C = 2\pi r$ $\qquad$ (r)

2   $k = \dfrac{PV}{T}$ $\qquad$ (V)

3   $ax + b = 2x + 3b$ $\qquad$ (x)

4   $a(x - y) = 3(x + y)$ $\qquad$ (x)

5   $pq - r = rq - t$ $\qquad$ (p)

6   $pq - r = rq - t$ $\qquad$ (q)

7   $pq - r = rq - t$ $\qquad$ (r)

8   $s = \frac{1}{2}(u + v)t$ $\qquad$ (t)

9   $s = \frac{1}{2}(u + v)t$ $\qquad$ (v)

10 $V = \dfrac{1}{x} - \dfrac{1}{3}$ $\qquad$ (x)

Exercise 16.2H

1   Rearrange each of these formulae to make the letter in brackets the subject.
   (a) $y = 2x^2 + 3$ $\qquad$ (x)
   (b) $h = \dfrac{gt^2}{4\pi^2}$ $\qquad$ (t)
   (c) $y = \sqrt{\dfrac{x}{3}}$ $\qquad$ (x)
   (d) $y = \sqrt{x + a}$ $\qquad$ (x)
   (e) $s = \sqrt{x^2 + y^2}$ $\qquad$ (x)
   (f) $A = \frac{1}{3}\pi r (l + 3r)$ $\qquad$ (l)
   (g) $y = \dfrac{2x}{3} - 5$ $\qquad$ (x)
   (h) $y = (x - a)^2$ $\qquad$ (x)

2   The formula for the volume of a sphere is $V = \frac{4}{3}\pi r^3$ where r is the radius of the sphere.
   (a) Find the volume of a sphere of radius 3 cm. Give your answer to 1 decimal place.
   (b) Rearrange the formula to make r the subject.
   (c) What is the radius of a sphere with volume 500 cm³? Give your answer to 1 decimal place.

3   The formula for the geometric mean, m, of two numbers, a and b, is $m = \sqrt{ab}$.
   For three numbers, a, b and c, the geometric mean is $m = \sqrt[3]{abc}$, and for four numbers, a, b, c and d, it is $\sqrt[4]{abcd}$.
   (a) Use the appropriate formula to find the geometric mean of the numbers 5, 8 and 12. Give your answer correct to 2 decimal places.
   (b) The geometric mean of four numbers 4, 7, 8 and x is 6.88, correct to 2 decimal places.
      (i) Rearrange the appropriate formula to make x the subject.
      (ii) Find x correct to the nearest whole number.

Unit B Contents

1   Properties of shapes   44

2   Fractions, decimals and percentages   47

3   Mental methods   50

4   Transformations   52

5   Straight–line graphs   57

6   Indices, decimals and surds   61

7   Inequalities   63

8   Congruency   64

9   Simultaneous equations   66

10 Vectors   68

11 Circle theorems   71

12 Scatter diagrams and time series   74

Unit C   77

1 Properties of shapes

Exercise 1.1H

Find the size of the lettered angles.
Give a reason for each answer.

1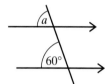

2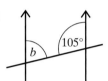

3

4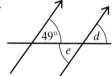

5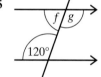

6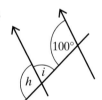

7

8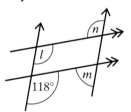

9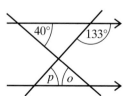

10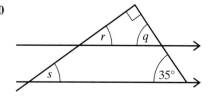

Exercise 1.2H

Find the size of the lettered angles.
Give a reason for each answer.

1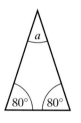

2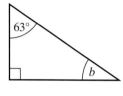

3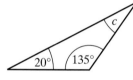

4

5

6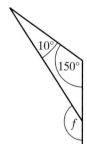

7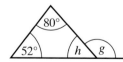

8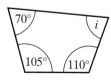

9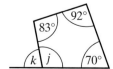

10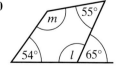

Exercise 1.3H

1 Name each of these quadrilaterals.

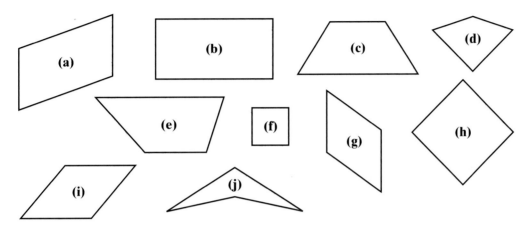

2 Name the quadrilateral or quadrilaterals which have the following properties.
  (a) Four right angles
  (b) Both pairs of opposite sides parallel
  (c) Equal diagonals
  (d) At least one pair of opposite sides parallel
  (e) Diagonals that bisect each other

3 Plot each set of points on squared paper and join them in order to make a quadrilateral.
  Use a different grid for each part.
  Write down the special name of each quadrilateral.
  (a) (3, 0), (5, 2), (3, 4), (1, 2)
  (b) (2, 1), (4, 1), (4, 5), (2, 5)
  (c) (1, 2), (3, 1), (3, 6), (1, 7)
  (d) (2, 1), (2, 5), (8, 4), (8, 2)

4 A rhombus is a special type of parallelogram.
  What extra properties does a rhombus have?

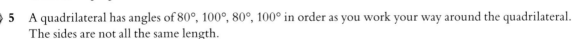 **5** A quadrilateral has angles of 80°, 100°, 80°, 100° in order as you work your way around the quadrilateral.
  The sides are not all the same length.
  Which special quadrilateral could have these angles?
  Draw the quadrilateral and mark on the angles.

Exercise 1.4H

1 A polygon has nine sides.
   Work out the sum of the interior angles of this polygon.

2 A polygon has 13 sides.
   Work out the sum of the interior angles of this polygon.

3 Four of the exterior angles of a hexagon are 93°, 50°, 37° and 85°.
   The other two angles are equal.
   (a) Work out the size of these equal exterior angles.
   (b) Work out the size of the interior angles of the hexagon.

4 Four of the interior angles of a pentagon are 170°, 80°, 157°, and 75°.
   (a) Work out the size of the other interior angle.
   (b) Work out the size of the exterior angles of the pentagon.

5 A regular polygon has 18 sides.
   Find the size of the exterior and interior angles of this polygon.

6 A regular polygon has 24 sides.
   Find the size of the exterior and interior angles of this polygon.

7 A regular polygon has an exterior angle of 12°.
   Work out the number of sides the polygon has.

8 A regular polygon has an interior angle of 172°.
   Work out the number of sides the polygon has.

9 Six of the angles of a heptagon are 113°, 142°, 125°, 109°, 128° and 157°.
   Calculate the size of the remaining angle.

10 What is the sum of the interior angles of a decagon?

11 A polygon has 12 sides.
    Eleven of its interior angles add up to 1685°.
    Find the size of the remaining angle.

12 A regular hexagon is constructed in a circle.
    How many degrees are measured at the centre to draw each radius required?

13 A 20-sided regular polygon is constructed in a circle.
    How many degrees are measured at the centre to draw each radius required?

14 Draw a circle of radius 5 cm and use it to construct a regular pentagon.
    Measure the length of a side of your pentagon.

15 Draw a circle of radius 6 cm and use it to construct a regular nine-sided polygon.
    Measure the length of a side of your polygon.

2 Fractions, decimals and percentages

Exercise 2.1H

1 For each pair of fractions
 • find the lowest common denominator.
 • state which is the bigger fraction.
 (a) $\frac{7}{8}$ or $\frac{3}{4}$ (b) $\frac{5}{9}$ or $\frac{7}{11}$ (c) $\frac{1}{6}$ or $\frac{3}{20}$

2 Work out these.
 (a) $\frac{3}{7} + \frac{2}{7}$ (b) $\frac{7}{15} + \frac{4}{15}$ (c) $\frac{8}{11} - \frac{3}{11}$
 (d) $\frac{11}{17} - \frac{8}{17}$ (e) $\frac{7}{16} + \frac{3}{16}$ (f) $\frac{7}{9} + \frac{4}{9}$
 (g) $\frac{7}{12} - \frac{5}{12}$ (h) $\frac{8}{11} + \frac{5}{11}$ (i) $2\frac{4}{7} + 3\frac{1}{7}$
 (j) $4\frac{5}{6} - 1\frac{1}{6}$ (k) $5\frac{9}{13} - \frac{4}{13}$ (l) $4\frac{3}{8} - 1\frac{5}{8}$

3 Work out these.
 (a) $\frac{2}{9} + \frac{1}{3}$ (b) $\frac{7}{12} + \frac{1}{4}$ (c) $\frac{3}{4} - \frac{1}{10}$
 (d) $\frac{13}{16} - \frac{3}{8}$ (e) $\frac{7}{8} + \frac{1}{3}$ (f) $\frac{4}{5} + \frac{5}{6}$
 (g) $\frac{7}{12} - \frac{1}{8}$ (h) $\frac{9}{20} + \frac{3}{4}$ (i) $\frac{7}{11} + \frac{3}{5}$
 (j) $\frac{7}{12} + \frac{7}{10}$ (k) $\frac{7}{8} - \frac{1}{6}$ (l) $\frac{7}{15} - \frac{3}{20}$

4 Work out these.
 (a) $4\frac{1}{4} + 3\frac{1}{3}$ (b) $6\frac{8}{9} - 1\frac{2}{3}$ (c) $5\frac{3}{8} + \frac{1}{4}$
 (d) $5\frac{11}{16} - 2\frac{1}{8}$ (e) $2\frac{5}{6} + 3\frac{1}{4}$ (f) $6\frac{8}{9} - 2\frac{1}{6}$
 (g) $3\frac{5}{8} + 4\frac{7}{10}$ (h) $5\frac{7}{11} - 5\frac{1}{3}$ (i) $4\frac{3}{4} + 3\frac{2}{7}$
 (j) $6\frac{1}{4} - 2\frac{2}{3}$ (k) $7\frac{1}{9} - 2\frac{1}{2}$ (l) $5\frac{3}{10} - 4\frac{4}{5}$

5 A desk is $27\frac{1}{4}$ inches high.
 A stand $2\frac{3}{5}$ inches high is placed on the desk for the computer.
 What is the height of the top of the computer stand above the floor?

6 Jo cut two pieces of string $8\frac{7}{8}$ inches and $9\frac{3}{4}$ inches long from a piece 30 inches long.
 How long was the piece that was left?

7 Fred baked two sponge cakes of the same size for his café.
 On the first day three-fifths of one of them was eaten.
 On the second day one and one-eighth of the cakes were eaten.
 What fraction of a cake was left for the third day?

8 Chris had a box of chocolates.
 $\frac{2}{5}$ were milk chocolate, $\frac{1}{4}$ were white chocolate and the rest were plain chocolate.
 What fraction were plain chocolate?

9 In a French spelling test Pete got $\frac{13}{15}$ of the answers correct and Tim got $\frac{9}{10}$ of the answers correct.
 Who did better in the test and by what fraction?

Exercise 2.2H

1 Change these mixed numbers to improper fractions.
 (a) $4\frac{3}{5}$ (b) $6\frac{1}{4}$ (c) $3\frac{4}{7}$
 (d) $1\frac{5}{9}$ (e) $4\frac{5}{6}$ (f) $7\frac{3}{10}$
 (g) $4\frac{7}{8}$

2 Work out these.
 Write your answers as proper fractions or mixed numbers in their lowest terms.
 (a) $\frac{3}{7} \times 5$ (b) $\frac{5}{9} \times 6$ (c) $\frac{3}{5} \div 4$
 (d) $6 \times \frac{5}{11}$ (e) $\frac{2}{9} \div 4$ (f) $9 \div \frac{3}{8}$

3 Work out these.
 Write your answers as proper fractions or mixed numbers in their lowest terms.
 (a) $\frac{2}{3} \times \frac{5}{7}$ (b) $\frac{1}{8} \times \frac{5}{6}$ (c) $\frac{7}{9} \times \frac{2}{5}$
 (d) $\frac{5}{8} \div \frac{3}{4}$ (e) $\frac{3}{8} \div \frac{1}{3}$ (f) $\frac{4}{9} \times \frac{5}{11}$
 (g) $\frac{6}{7} \times \frac{1}{8}$ (h) $\frac{7}{15} \div \frac{2}{3}$ (i) $\frac{7}{12} \times \frac{3}{8}$
 (j) $\frac{9}{16} \div \frac{7}{12}$ (k) $\frac{7}{10} \div \frac{5}{12}$ (l) $\frac{7}{30} \times \frac{10}{21}$

4   Work out these.
    Write your answers as proper fractions or mixed
    numbers in their lowest terms.

(a) $4\frac{3}{4} \times 1\frac{7}{9}$ (b) $3\frac{2}{3} \times \frac{1}{5}$ (c) $4\frac{2}{5} \div 2\frac{4}{5}$

(d) $1\frac{3}{11} \div 3\frac{1}{2}$ (e) $4\frac{1}{2} \times 3\frac{2}{3}$ (f) $3\frac{5}{9} \div 2\frac{2}{3}$

(g) $3\frac{2}{7} \times 1\frac{5}{9}$ (h) $2\frac{5}{8} \div 1\frac{5}{6}$ (i) $1\frac{7}{15} \times 12\frac{1}{2}$

(j) $5\frac{3}{5} \div 1\frac{3}{4}$ (k) $6\frac{2}{9} \times 2\frac{1}{8}$ (l) $7\frac{1}{2} \div 2\frac{3}{5}$

5   Work out these.

(a) $4\frac{1}{2} + 3\frac{3}{4} \times 2\frac{2}{3}$

(b) $\left(6\frac{3}{4} - 2\frac{1}{5}\right) \div 4\frac{1}{3}$

 6   In an election, the Independent candidate got
    720 votes, which was $\frac{4}{9}$ of the votes.
    The Green candidate got $\frac{1}{6}$ of the votes.
    How many votes did the Green candidate get?

7   A rectangular pond is $3\frac{1}{3}$ m long and has an area
    of $7\frac{1}{2}$ m^2.
    Find the width of the pond.

 8   David has some savings.
    He spends £13 on a DVD and $\frac{2}{5}$ of the rest on
    sweets.
    He has £21 left.
    How much were his savings?

Exercise 2.3H

Work out these.

1   3.4 + 6.1   2   4.3 + 3.6

3   5.8 − 2.3   4   7.9 − 4.4

5   3.7 + 2.6   6   5.8 + 3.4

7   7.2 − 0.9   8   5.4 − 3.5

9   6.28 + 8.93   10   9.87 + 2.34

11   7.35 − 4.82   12   8.12 − 7.49

13   6.09 + 7.93   14   4.57 + 2.84

15   7.02 − 5.38   16   2.04 − 1.85

Exercise 2.4H

1   Work out these.

(a) 5×0.4 (b) 0.6×8

(c) 4×0.7 (d) 0.9×6

(e) 0.7×0.3 (f) 0.9×0.4

(g) 50×0.7 (h) 0.4×80

(i) 0.7×0.1 (j) 0.4×0.2

(k) $(0.8)^2$ (l) $(0.2)^2$

2   Work out these.

(a) $6 \div 0.3$ (b) $4.8 \div 0.2$

(c) $2.4 \div 0.6$ (d) $7.2 \div 0.4$

(e) $33 \div 1.1$ (f) $60 \div 1.5$

(g) $12 \div 0.4$ (h) $35 \div 0.7$

(i) $64 \div 0.8$ (j) $32 \div 0.2$

(k) $2.17 \div 0.7$ (l) $47.5 \div 0.5$

3   Work out these.

(a) 3.6×1.4 (b) 5.8×2.6

(c) 8.1×4.3 (d) 6.5×3.2

(e) 74×1.7 (f) 64×3.8

(g) 2.9×7.6 (h) 11.4×3.2

(i) 25.2×0.8 (j) 2.67×0.9

(k) 8.45×1.2 (l) 7.26×2.4

4   Work out these.

(a) $23.6 \div 0.4$ (b) $23.4 \div 0.8$

(c) $18.2 \div 0.7$ (d) $31.2 \div 0.6$

(e) $42.3 \div 0.9$ (f) $75.6 \div 1.2$

(g) $5.28 \div 0.3$ (h) $7.56 \div 0.7$

(i) $63.2 \div 0.2$ (j) $6.27 \div 1.1$

(k) $3.51 \div 1.3$ (l) $8.19 \div 1.3$

Exercise 2.5H

1   Write down the multiplier that will increase an
    amount by
    (a) 17%.   **(b)** 30%.   **(c)** 73%.
    (d) 6%.   **(e)** 1%.   **(f)** 12.5%.
    (g) 160%.

2   Write down the multiplier that will decrease an
    amount by
    (a) 13%.   **(b)** 40%.   **(c)** 35%.
    (d) 8%.   **(e)** 4%.   **(f)** 27%.
    (g) 15.5%.

3   Mrs Green bought an antique for £200.
    She later sold it at 250% profit.
    What did she sell it for?

4   Jane earns £14 500 per year.
    She receives an increase of 2%.
    Find her new salary.

5   In a sale all items are reduced by 20%.
    Shamir bought a computer in the sale.
    The original price was £490.
    What was the sale price?

6   An Easter egg manufacturer sold a 200 g Easter
    egg for £5.
    He needed to increase his profits.
    He could either
    •   increase the price by 20% or
    •   reduce the weight of the egg by 20%.
    Which is more profitable?

7   A train company increases its fares by 16%.
    All new fares that are less than £50 will be
    rounded to the nearest £5.
    All new fares that are more than £50 will be
    rounded to the nearest £10.
    Find the new fare when the old fare is
    (a) £36.   **(b)** £85.

Mental methods

Exercise 3.1H

Work these out mentally. As far as possible, write down only the final answer.

1 (a) $8 + 25$ (b) $13 + 49$
  (c) $0.6 + 5.2$ (d) $142 + 59$
  (e) $187 + 25$ (f) $5.8 + 12.6$
  (g) $326 + 9.3$ (h) $456 + 83$
  (i) $1290 + 41$ (j) $8600 + 570$

2 (a) $12 - 5$ (b) $36 - 9$
  (c) $10 - 0.4$ (d) $56 - 45$
  (e) $82 - 39$ (f) $141 - 27$
  (g) $1.2 - 0.7$ (h) $186 - 19$
  (i) $307 - 81$ (j) $1200 - 153$

3 (a) 7×9 (b) 12×8
  (c) 22×7 (d) 11×12
  (e) 0.4×100 (f) 19×7
  (g) 48×5 (h) 25×8
  (i) 63×4 (j) 42×21

4 (a) $42 \div 7$ (b) $72 \div 12$
  (c) $1500 \div 3$ (d) $184 \div 8$
  (e) $240 \div 20$ (f) $108 \div 18$
  (g) $96 \div 16$ (h) $16 \div 100$
  (i) $24 \div 0.3$ (j) $3.6 \div 0.9$

5 (a) $7 + (-3)$ (b) $-2 + 6$
  (c) $-5 + 7$ (d) $-4 + (-8)$
  (e) $4 + (-9)$ (f) $-5 - 1$
  (g) $6 - (-2)$ (h) $12 - (-8)$
  (i) $-5 - (-10)$ (j) $-7 - (-3)$

6 (a) 12×-2 (b) -4×5
  (c) -6×-3 (d) -10×-4
  (e) 4×-100 (f) $10 \div -5$
  (g) $-6 \div 2$ (h) $-20 \div -4$
  (i) $-35 \div -5$ (j) $32 \div -4$

7 Write down the square of each of these numbers.
  (a) 7   (b) 9   (c) 12
  (d) 14   (e) 1   (f) 30
  (g) 200   (h) 0.5   (i) 0.8
  (j) 0.2

8 Write down the square roots of each of these numbers.
  (a) 36   (b) 4   (c) 64
  (d) 121   (e) 144

9 Write down the cube of each of these numbers.
  (a) 3   (b) 4   (c) 10
  (d) 50   (e) 0.2

10 A rectangle has sides of 4.6 cm and 5.0 cm. Work out
  (a) the perimeter of the rectangle.
  (b) the area of the rectangle.

11 Ayeesha spends £17.81. How much change does she get from £50?

12 A square has an area of 121 cm². How long is its side?

13 Find 2% of £540.

14 Find two numbers the difference between which is 4 and the product 45.

15 Deepa has a 1 kg piece of cheese. She eats 432 g of it. How much is left?

16 In a sale a jacket costing £54 is reduced by 5%. Find the sale price of the jacket.

17 At a supermarket discount vouchers are given when more than £60 is spent. Kate's bill came to £49.26 so she decided to buy packs of dishwasher tablets at £5.29 each.
  (a) How many packs does she need to buy to reach £60?
  (b) How much over £60 does she spend?

18 Find the sum of the largest square number less than 130 and the largest cube less than 130.

Exercise 3.2H

For questions **1** to **9**, round the numbers in your calculations to 1 significant figure. Show your working.

1 Estimate the answers to these calculations.

(a) 71×58
(b) $\sqrt{46}$
(c) $\dfrac{5987}{5.1}$
(d) 19.1^2
(e) 62.7×8316
(f) $\dfrac{5.72}{19.3}$
(g) $\dfrac{32}{49.4}$
(h) 8152×37
(i) $\dfrac{935 \times 41}{8.5}$
(j) $\dfrac{6.73 \times 0.76}{3.6 \times 2.38}$

2 Ashad bought 24 chocolate bars at 32p each. Estimate how much he spent.

3 Ramy earns £382 per week. Estimate his earnings in a year.

4 Mary drove 215 miles in 3 hours 48 minutes. Estimate her average speed.

5 A new computer is priced at £595 excluding VAT. VAT at 17.5% must be paid on it. Estimate the amount of VAT to be paid.

6 A square paving slab has an area of 6000 cm^2. Estimate the length of a side of the slab.

7 32 members of the gardening club bought a bulk order of plants. The total cost of the plants was £576.99. Estimate how much each member paid on average.

8 Steve is buying a new carpet for his living room. The room is 3.58 m wide by 4.27 m long. The furnishers charge £3.75 per square metre to fit the carpet. Estimate the fitting charge.

9 Fazail wants to paint the ceiling of his discount store. The ceiling is 12.4 m by 7.8 m. A 5-litre tin of paint covers 31 m^2. Estimate how many 5-litre tins of paint he needs to buy.

10 Round each of these numbers to 2 significant figures.

(a) 28.7
(b) 149.3
(c) 7832
(d) 46 820
(e) 21.36
(f) 0.194
(g) 0.0489
(h) 0.003 61
(i) 0.0508
(j) 0.904

11 Round each of these numbers to 3 significant figures.

(a) 7.385
(b) 24.81
(c) 28 462
(d) 308.61
(e) 16 418
(f) 3.917
(g) 60.72
(h) 0.9135
(i) 0.004 162
(j) 2.236 06

Exercise 3.3H

1 Work out these.

(a) 0.06×600
(b) 0.03×0.3
(c) 0.9×0.04
(d) $(0.05)^2$
(e) $(0.3)^2$
(f) 500×800
(g) 30×5000
(h) 5.1×300
(i) 20.3×2000
(j) 1.82×5000

2 Work out these.

(a) $300 \div 20$
(b) $60 \div 2000$
(c) $3.6 \div 20$
(d) $1.4 \div 0.2$
(e) $2.4 \div 3000$
(f) $2.4 \div 0.03$
(g) $0.08 \div 0.004$
(h) $5 \div 0.02$
(i) $400 \div 0.08$
(j) $60 \div 0.15$

3 Given that $4.5 \times 16.8 = 75.6$, work out these.

(a) 45×1680
(b) $75.6 \div 168$
(c) $7560 \div 45$
(d) 0.168×0.045
(e) $756 \div 0.168$

4 Given that $702 \div 39 = 18$, work out these.

(a) $70\,200 \div 39$
(b) $70.2 \div 3.9$
(c) 180×39
(d) $7.02 \div 18$
(e) 1.8×3.9

5 Given that $348 \times 216 = 75\,168$, work out these.

(a) $751\,680 \div 216$
(b) $34\,800 \times 2160$
(c) 3.48×21.6
(d) $751.68 \div 34.8$
(e) 0.348×2160

Exercise 4.1H

1   Draw a pair of axes and label them −2 to 4 for
    x and y.
    (a) Draw a triangle with vertices at (1, 1), (1, 3)
        and (0, 3). Label it A.
    (b) Reflect triangle A in the line $x = 2$.
        Label it B.
    (c) Reflect triangle A in the line $y = x$.
        Label it C.
    (d) Reflect triangle A in the line $y = 2$.
        Label it D.

2   Draw a pair of axes and label them −3 to 3 for
    x and y.
    (a) Draw a triangle with vertices at (−1, 1),
        (−1, 3) and (−2, 3). Label it A.
    (b) Reflect triangle A in the line $x = \frac{1}{2}$. Label it B.
    (c) Reflect triangle A in the line $y = x$. Label it C.
    (d) Reflect triangle A in the line $y = -x$. Label it D.

3   For each part
    • copy the diagram.
    • reflect the shape in the mirror line.

    (a)   (b)
    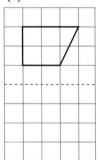   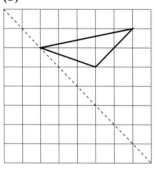

    (c)
    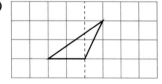

4   Describe fully the single transformation that maps
    (a) shape A on to shape B.
    (b) shape A on to shape C.
    (c) shape B on to shape D.

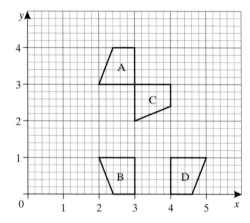

5   Describe fully the single transformation that maps
    (a) triangle A on to triangle B.
    (b) triangle A on to triangle C.
    (c) triangle E on to triangle F.

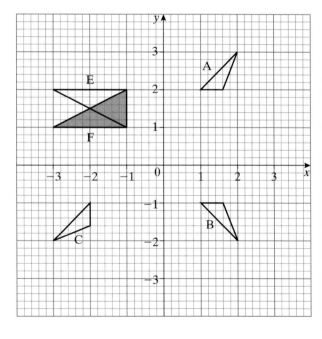

Exercise 4.2H

1 Copy the diagram.

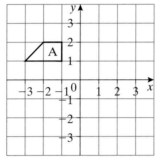

(a) Rotate shape A through 180° about the origin. Label it B.

(b) Rotate shape A through 90° clockwise about the point (0, 1). Label it C.

(c) Rotate shape A through 90° anticlockwise about the point (−1, 1). Label it D.

2 Copy the diagram.

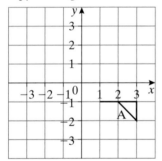

(a) Rotate flag A through 90° clockwise about the origin. Label it B.

(b) Rotate flag A through 90° anticlockwise about the point (1, −1). Label it C.

(c) Rotate flag A through 180° about the point (0, −1). Label it D.

3 Draw a pair of axes and label them −4 to 4 for x and y.

(a) Draw a triangle with vertices at (1, 1), (2, 1) and (2, 3). Label it A.

(b) Rotate triangle A through 90° anticlockwise about the origin. Label it B.

(c) Rotate triangle A through 180° about the point (2, 1). Label it C.

(d) Rotate triangle A through 90° clockwise about the point (−2, 1). Label it D.

4 Describe fully the single transformation that maps

(a) trapezium A on to trapezium B.

(b) trapezium A on to trapezium C.

(c) trapezium A on to trapezium D.

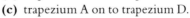
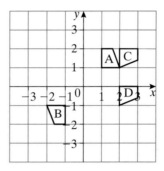

5 Describe fully the single transformation that maps

(a) flag A on to flag B.

(b) flag A on to flag C.

(c) flag A on to flag D.

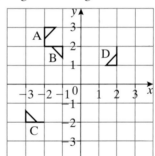

6 Describe fully the single transformation that maps triangle A on to triangle B.

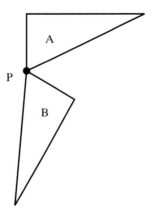

7 Describe fully the single transformation that maps
  (a) triangle A on to triangle B.
  (b) triangle A on to triangle C.
  (c) triangle A on to triangle D.
  (d) triangle A on to triangle E.
  (e) triangle A on to triangle F.

  Hint: Some of these transformations are reflections.

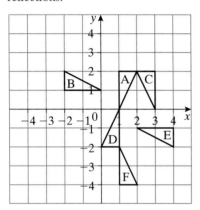

Exercise 4.3H

1 Draw a pair of axes and label them −2 to 6 for *x* and *y*.
  (a) Draw a triangle with vertices at (1, 1), (1, 2), and (4, 1). Label it A.
  (b) Translate A by vector $\begin{pmatrix} 1 \\ 3 \end{pmatrix}$. Label it B.
  (c) Translate A by vector $\begin{pmatrix} -3 \\ 4 \end{pmatrix}$. Label it C.
  (d) Translate A by vector $\begin{pmatrix} -2 \\ -3 \end{pmatrix}$. Label it D.

2 Draw a pair of axes and label them −3 to 5 for *x* and *y*.
  (a) Draw a triangle with vertices at (2, 1), (2, 3) and (3, 1). Label it A.
  (b) Translate A by vector $\begin{pmatrix} 2 \\ 1 \end{pmatrix}$. Label it B.
  (c) Translate A by vector $\begin{pmatrix} -5 \\ -3 \end{pmatrix}$. Label it C.
  (d) Translate A by vector $\begin{pmatrix} 2 \\ -4 \end{pmatrix}$. Label it D.

3 Describe the single transformation that maps
  (a) triangle A on to triangle B.
  (b) triangle A on to triangle C.
  (c) triangle A on to triangle D.
  (d) triangle B on to triangle D.

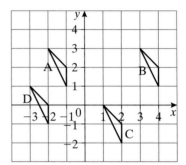

4 Describe the single transformation that maps
  (a) shape A on to shape B.
  (b) shape A on to shape C.
  (c) shape A on to shape D.
  (d) shape D on to shape E.
  (e) shape A on to shape F.
  (f) shape E on to shape G.
  (g) shape B on to shape H.
  (h) shape H on to shape F.

  Hint: Not all the transformations are translations.

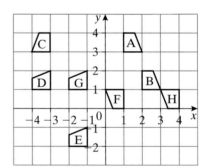

Exercise 4.4H

1 Draw a pair of axes and label them 0 to 6 for both *x* and *y*.
  (a) Draw a triangle with vertices at (0, 6), (3, 6) and (3, 3). Label it A.
  (b) Enlarge triangle A by scale factor $\frac{1}{3}$, with the origin as the centre of enlargement. Label it B.

(c) Describe fully the single transformation that maps triangle B on to triangle A.

2 Draw a pair of axes and label them 0 to 6 for both x and y.
  (a) Draw a triangle with vertices at (5, 2), (5, 6) and (3, 6). Label it A.
  (b) Enlarge triangle A by scale factor $\frac{1}{2}$, with centre of enlargement (3, 2). Label it B.
  (c) Describe fully the single transformation that maps triangle B on to triangle A.

3 Draw a pair of axes and label them 0 to 8 for both x and y.
  (a) Draw a triangle with vertices at (2, 1), (2, 3) and (3, 2). Label it A.
  (b) Enlarge triangle A by scale factor $2\frac{1}{2}$, with the origin as the centre of enlargement. Label it B.
  (c) Describe fully the single transformation that maps triangle B on to triangle A.

4 Draw a pair of axes and label them 0 to 7 for both x and y.
  (a) Draw a trapezium with vertices at (1, 2), (1, 3), (2, 3) and (3, 2). Label it A.
  (b) Enlarge triangle A by scale factor 3, with centre of enlargement (1, 2). Label it B.
  (c) Describe fully the single transformation that maps triangle B on to triangle A.

5 Describe fully the single transformation that maps
  (a) triangle A on to triangle B.
  (b) triangle B on to triangle A.
  (c) triangle A on to triangle C.
  (d) triangle C on to triangle A.

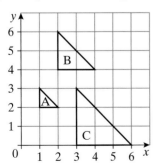

Hint: In question **6**, not all the transformation are enlargements.

6 Describe fully the single transformation that maps
  (a) flag A on to flag B.   **(b)** flag B on to flag C.
  (c) flag B on to flag D.   **(d)** flag B on to flag E.
  (e) flag F on to flag G.

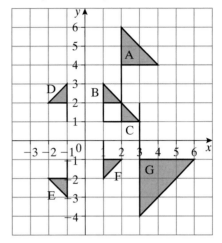

7 Draw a pair of axes and label them −4 to 4 for x and y.
  (a) Draw a triangle with vertices at (2, 1), (2, 2) and (4, 2). Label it A.
  (b) Reflect A in the line $y = 0$. Label it B.
  (c) Reflect A in the line $x = 1$. Label it C.
  (d) Rotate B by 90° about the origin. Label it D.
  (e) Enlarge A by scale factor $\frac{1}{2}$, with the origin as the centre of enlargement. Label it E.

8 Copy the diagram.

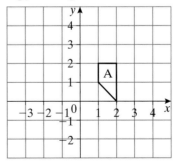

  (a) Rotate shape A through 90° clockwise about the origin. Label it B.
  (b) Rotate shape A through 180° about (2, 2). Label it C.
  (c) Enlarge shape A by scale factor $\frac{1}{2}$, with centre of enlargement (−2, 0). Label it E.

Exercise 4.5H

1 Draw a pair of axes with the x-axis from −8 to 16 and the y-axis from −6 to 10.
   Plot the points A(−2, −1), B(−2, −4) and C(−7, −1) and join them to form a triangle.
   Enlarge the triangle by a scale factor of −2 using the origin as the centre of enlargement.

2 Draw a pair of axes and label them −8 to 8 and for x and y.
   Plot the points A(6, 5), B(6, 8) and C(8, 8) and join them to form a triangle.
   Enlarge the triangle by a scale factor of −3 using (4, 4) as the centre of enlargement.

3 The diagram shows a quadrilateral, ABCD, and its image A′B′C′D′.

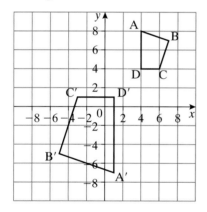

   Copy the diagram and find
   (a) the centre of enlargement.
   (b) the scale factor.

4 Draw a pair of axes with the x-axis from −10 to 10 and the y-axis from −8 to 8.
   Plot the points A(−4, 3), B(−4, −3) and C(−10, −5) and join them to form a triangle.
   Enlarge the triangle by a scale factor of $-\frac{1}{2}$ using (2, 3) as the centre of enlargement.

5 The diagram shows a triangle, ABC, and its image A′B′C′.

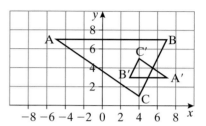

   Copy the diagram and find
   (a) the centre of enlargement.
   (b) the scale factor.

Exercise 4.6H

In questions **1** to **6** carry out the transformations on the triangle ABC where A is (1, 1), B is (1, 3) and C is (2, 3).
Describe fully the single transformation equivalent to each of these sets of transformations.

1 Reflection in the line $y = 0$ followed by rotation through 180° about the point (3, 0)

2 Translation by the vector $\begin{pmatrix} 0 \\ -3 \end{pmatrix}$ followed by enlargement with scale factor 2 and centre the origin.

3 Reflection in the line $y = x$ followed by rotation through 90° anticlockwise about the origin.

4 Translation by vector $\begin{pmatrix} 3 \\ 1 \end{pmatrix}$ followed by rotation through 90° clockwise about the point (5, 1).

5 Rotation through 180° about the point (1, 1) followed by enlargement with scale factor 3 and centre (1, 1).

6 Reflection in the y-axis followed by rotation through 180° about the point (−1, 1) followed by reflection in the line $y = 2$.

7 Carry out the following transformations on a simple shape of your choice.
   Describe fully the single transformation that is equivalent to a rotation through 90° anticlockwise about the origin followed by a reflection in the x-axis.

Chapter 5

Straight-line graphs

Exercise 5.1H

1   Draw the graph of $y = 3x$ for values of x from −3 to 3.

2   Draw the graph of $y = x + 2$ for values of x from −4 to 2.

3   Draw the graph of $y = 4x + 2$ for values of x from −3 to 3.

4   Draw the graph of $y = 2x - 5$ for values of x from −1 to 5.

5   Draw the graph of $y = -2x - 4$ for values of x from −4 to 2.

Exercise 5.2H

1   Draw the graph of $3y = 2x + 6$ for values of x from −3 to 3.

2   Draw the graph of $2x + 5y = 10$.

3   Draw the graph of $3x + 2y = 15$.

4   Draw the graph of $2y = 5x - 8$, for values of x from −2 to 4.

5   Draw the graph of $3x + 4y = 24$.

6   (a) Draw a distance–time graph to show this cycle ride.
        Use a scale of 1 cm for 30 minutes and 1 cm for 5 km.
        Robert left home at 9 am and cycled 12 km in the next 45 minutes.
        He then stopped for 15 minutes.
        He continued his journey and went 10 km in the next 45 minutes.
        After a half hour's break he cycled directly home, ariving there at 1 pm.
    (b) Use your graph to answer these questions.
        (i)   How long did it take Robert to cycle back home?
        (ii) How far did he cycle altogether?
        (iii) What was his speed on the first section of his journey?

Exercise 5.3H

1   Find the gradient of each of these lines.

(a)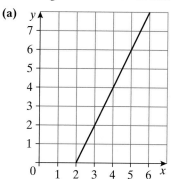

(b)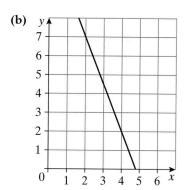

(c)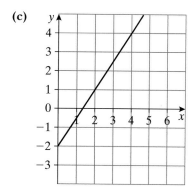

2 Find the gradient of the line joining each of these pairs of points.
   (a) (1, 2) and (3, 8)   **(b)** (5, 1) and (7, 3)
   (c) (0, 3) and (2, –3)   **(d)** (–1, 4) and (3, 2)
   (e) (3, –1) and (–1, –1)

3 Find the gradient of each side of the triangle ABC.

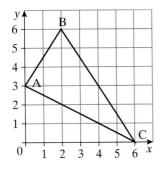

4 Find the gradient of each of these lines.

(a)
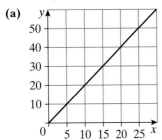

(b)
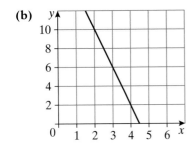

(c)
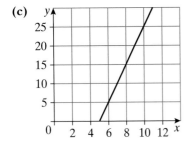

5 Draw the graph of each of these straight lines and find its gradient.
   (a) $y = 3x + 1$
   (b) $y = x - 2$
   (c) $y = -3x + 2$
   (d) $y = -2x - 1$
   (e) $3x + 4y = 12$

6 Find the speed for each of these distance–time graphs.

(a)
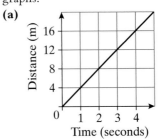

(b)
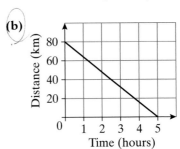

Exercise 5.4H

1   Write down the equations of straight lines with these gradients and y-intercepts.
   (a) Gradient 2, y-intercept 6
   (b) Gradient −3, y-intercept 5
   (c) Gradient 1, y-intercept 0

2   Find the equation of each of these lines.
   (a)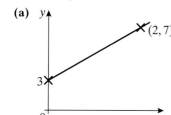
   (b)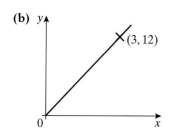
   (c)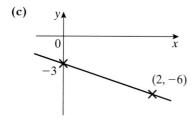

3   Find the gradient and y-intercept of each of these lines.
   (a) $y = 4x − 2$ (b) $y = 3x + 5$
   (c) $y = −2x + 1$ (d) $y = −x + 2$
   (e) $y = −3.5x − 8$

4   Find the gradient and y-intercept of each of these lines.
   (a) $y + 3x = 7$ (b) $6x + 2y = 5$
   (c) $2x + y = 3$ (d) $5x − 2y = 8$
   (e) $6x + 4y = 9$

5   Find the equation of each of these lines.
   (a)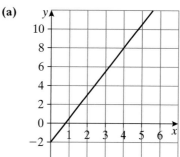
   (b)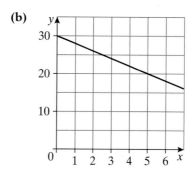
   (c)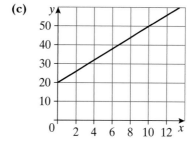

6   Find the equation of each of these straight lines.
   (a) A line with gradient $\frac{3}{4}$, passing through the point (4, 2).
   (b) A line passing through (1, 3) and (4, 9).
   (c) A line passing through (2, 3) and (5, −6).
   (d) A line passing through (−1, 5) and (3, −5).
   (e) A line passing through (3, 1) and (−3, −7).

Exercise 5.5H

1 Find the gradient of a line perpendicular to the line joining each of these pairs of points.
   (a) (1, 1) and (5, 3)
   (b) (1, 2) and (4, −2)
   (c) (−1, 5) and (2, 8)

2 Find the equation of the line that passes through (1, 0) and is parallel to $y = 2x + 6$.

3 Find the equation of the line that passes through (2, 3) and is parallel to $4x + 2y = 7$.

4 (a) State the gradient of the line $3x + 5y = 6$.
   (b) Find the equation of the line perpendicular to $3x + 5y = 6$ that passes through (1, 1).

5 Find the equation of the line that passes through (4, 1) and is perpendicular to $y = 4x + 3$.

6 Find the equation of the line that passes through (0, 5) and is perpendicular to $3y = x − 1$.

7 Find the equation of the line that passes through (2, 5) and is perpendicular to $7y + 2x = 9$.

8 Which of these lines are
   (a) parallel?
   (b) perpendicular?
   $$y = x + 5$$
   $$y = 3x + 5$$
   $$x + 3y = 5$$
   $$4x − y = 5$$

 9 Two lines cross at right angles at the point (2, 5). One passes through (4, 7). What is the equation of the other line?

10 In the diagram AC is a diagonal of the square ABCD. Work out
   (a) the equation of the line AC.
   (b) the equation of the line BD.
   (c) the coordinates of B and D.

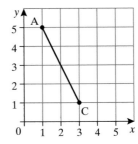

6 Indices, decimals and surds

Exercise 6.1H

1 Write these in simpler form using indices.
(a) $2 \times 2 \times 2 \times 2 \times 2 \times 2$
(b) $7 \times 7 \times 7 \times 7$
(c) $2 \times 2 \times 3 \times 3 \times 3 \times 3 \times 5 \times 5 \times 5$
Hint: Write the different numbers separately.

2 Work out these, giving your answers in index form.
(a) $2^2 \times 2^4$ (b) $3^6 \times 3^2$
(c) $4^2 \times 4^3$ (d) $5^6 \times 5$

3 Work out these, giving your answers in index form.
(a) $5^5 \div 5^2$ (b) $7^8 \div 7^2$
(c) $2^6 \div 2^4$ (d) $3^7 \div 3^3$

4 Work out these, giving your answers in index form.
(a) $5^5 \times 5^3 \div 5^2$ (b) $10^4 \times 10^6 \div 10^5$
(c) $8^3 \times 8^3 \div 8^4$ (d) $3^5 \times 3 \div 3^3$

5 Work out these, giving your answers in index form.
(a) $\dfrac{2^5 \times 2^4}{2^3}$ (b) $\dfrac{3^7}{3^5 \times 3^2}$
(c) $\dfrac{5^5 \times 5^4}{5^2 \times 5^3}$ (d) $\dfrac{7^5 \times 7^2}{7^2 \times 7^4}$

6 Write these in index form.
(a) $\sqrt[5]{x}$
(b) The reciprocal of $x^{\frac{1}{2}}$
(c) $\sqrt[4]{x^3}$

7 Work out these. Give your answers as whole numbers or fractions.
(a) 25^{-1} (b) $25^{\frac{1}{2}}$ (c) 25^0
(d) $25^{-\frac{1}{2}}$ (e) $25^{\frac{3}{2}}$ (f) $27^{\frac{2}{3}}$
(g) $10\,000^{\frac{1}{4}}$ (h) $\left(\frac{1}{100}\right)^{-\frac{1}{2}}$ (i) $32^{\frac{6}{5}}$
(j) $\left(\frac{1}{2}\right)^0$ (k) $16^{\frac{1}{2}}$ (l) 16^0
(m) $16^{\frac{3}{2}}$ (n) $16^{-\frac{1}{4}}$ (o) $16^{\frac{7}{4}}$
(p) $144^{\frac{1}{2}}$ (q) $\left(\frac{2}{5}\right)^{-2}$

8 Work out these. Give your answers as whole numbers or fractions.
(a) $1000^{\frac{2}{3}} \times 8^{\frac{2}{3}}$
(b) $100^{-\frac{1}{2}} \times 49^{\frac{3}{2}}$
(c) $4^{-2} \times 10^4 \times 25^{-\frac{1}{2}}$
(d) $4^3 + 16^{\frac{1}{2}} - \left(\frac{1}{5}\right)^{-2}$
(e) $10\,000^{\frac{1}{4}} + 125^{\frac{1}{3}} - 121^{\frac{1}{2}}$
(f) $\left(\frac{4}{5}\right)^2 \times 128^{-\frac{3}{7}}$

Exercise 6.2H

1 Write these as powers of 2 as simply as possible.
(a) 64   (b) $8^{\frac{2}{3}}$ (c) 0.25
(d) $2 \times \sqrt[3]{64}$ (e) $4^{\frac{n}{2}}$ (f) $2^{3n} \times 4^{\frac{n}{2}}$

2 Where possible, write these as powers of a prime number as simply as possible.
(a) 343   (b) $9^{\frac{2}{3}}$ (c) $64^{-\frac{2}{3}}$
(d) $16^{\frac{1}{2}} \times 64^{-\frac{2}{3}}$ (e) $2^6 + 2^3$ (f) $27 \div 81^{\frac{2}{3}}$
(g) $9^{3n} \times 3^{-n}$

3 Write each of these in the form $2^a \times 3^b$ or $2^a \times 3^b \times 5^c$.
(a) 60   (b) 192
(c) 600   (d) 648

4 Write each of these numbers as a product of powers of prime numbers.
(a) 15^3 (b) $25^2 \times 10^{\frac{1}{2}}$
(c) 40^n (d) $40^n \times 10$

Exercise 6.3H

1 Which of these fractions are equivalent to recurring decimals?

   (a) $\frac{1}{8}$ (b) $\frac{7}{30}$ (c) $\frac{4}{7}$

   (d) $\frac{5}{16}$ (e) $\frac{11}{120}$

2 Find the decimal equivalent of each of the fractions in question **1**.

3 When these fractions are written as decimals, which of them terminate?

   (a) $\frac{6}{40}$ (b) $\frac{7}{8}$ (c) $\frac{1}{6}$

   (d) $\frac{2}{75}$ (e) $\frac{11}{80}$

4 Find the decimal equivalent of each of the fractions in question **3**.

5 Find the fractional equivalent of each of these terminating decimals.
   Write each fraction in its simplest form.
   (a) 0.16   (b) 0.305
   (c) 0.625   (d) 0.408

6 Find the fractional equivalent of each of these recurring decimals.
   Write each fraction in its simplest form.
   (a) $0.\dot{3}$ (b) $0.\dot{8}$
   (c) $0.1\dot{5}$ (d) $0.7\dot{2}$

7 Find the fractional equivalent of each of these recurring decimals.
   Write each fraction in its simplest form.
   (a) $0.\dot{6}\dot{3}$ (b) $0.4\dot{7}$
   (c) $0.1\dot{5}$ (d) $0.3\dot{8}$

8 Find the fractional equivalent of each of these recurring decimals.
   Write each fraction in its simplest form.
   (a) $0.3\dot{0}\dot{6}$ (b) $0.4\dot{1}\dot{4}$
   (c) $0.0\dot{8}$ (d) $0.02\dot{7}$

Exercise 6.4H

1 Simplify these.

   (a) $\sqrt{7} + 3\sqrt{7}$ (b) $9\sqrt{5} - 2\sqrt{5}$
   (c) $4\sqrt{3} - \sqrt{3}$ (d) $\sqrt{3} \times 5\sqrt{3}$
   (e) $6\sqrt{2} \times \sqrt{5}$ (f) $3\sqrt{3} \times \sqrt{12}$

2 Write each of these expressions in the form $a\sqrt{b}$, where b is an integer which is as small as possible.

   (a) $\sqrt{18}$ (b) $3\sqrt{50}$
   (c) $5\sqrt{12}$ (d) $6\sqrt{20}$
   (e) $\sqrt{108}$ (f) $\sqrt{1250}$

3 Simplify these.

   (a) $\sqrt{18} + 4\sqrt{2}$ (b) $7\sqrt{3} - \sqrt{75}$
   (c) $\sqrt{12} + 3\sqrt{3}$ (d) $\sqrt{8} \times 3\sqrt{6}$
   (e) $\sqrt{21} \times \sqrt{12}$ (f) $2\sqrt{250} \times \sqrt{10}$

4 Expand and simplify these.

   (a) $\sqrt{2}(5 + \sqrt{2})$ (b) $\sqrt{3}(\sqrt{12} + \sqrt{2})$
   (c) $4\sqrt{5}(2 + \sqrt{45})$ (d) $3\sqrt{2}(\sqrt{18} + \sqrt{5})$

5 Rationalise the denominator and simplify each of these.

   (a) $\dfrac{15}{\sqrt{3}}$ (b) $\dfrac{4}{\sqrt{5}}$

   (c) $\dfrac{6}{5\sqrt{2}}$ (d) $\dfrac{6}{7\sqrt{12}}$

   (e) $\dfrac{6\sqrt{3}}{5\sqrt{2}}$ (f) $\dfrac{12\sqrt{10}}{11\sqrt{6}}$

6 Rationalise the denominator and simplify each of these.

   (a) $\dfrac{10 + 2\sqrt{5}}{\sqrt{5}}$ (b) $\dfrac{12 + \sqrt{3}}{4\sqrt{3}}$

   (c) $\dfrac{6 + 5\sqrt{2}}{\sqrt{2}}$ (d) $\dfrac{5 + 10\sqrt{3}}{\sqrt{15}}$

Exercise 7.1H

For each of questions **1** to **5**, solve the inequality and show the solution on a number line.

1 $x - 2 > 1$

2 $x + 1 < 3$

3 $3x - 2 \geqslant 7$

4 $2x + 1 \leqslant 6$

5 $3x - 6 \geqslant 0$

For each of questions **6** to **21**, solve the inequality.

6 $7 \leqslant 2x - 1$

7 $5x < x + 12$

8 $4x \geqslant x + 9$

9 $4 + x < 0$

10 $3x + 1 \leqslant 2x + 6$

11 $2(x - 3) > x$

12 $5(x + 1) > 3x + 10$

13 $7x + 5 \leqslant 2x + 30$

14 $5x + 2 < 7x - 4$

15 $3(3x + 2) \geqslant 2(x + 10)$

16 $5(x - 2) > 11 - 2x$

17 $4(3x - 4) \geqslant 3(2x - 1) + 2$

18 $\dfrac{5x}{2} < x + 6$

19 $\dfrac{2x}{3} + 5 < 4x$

20 $\dfrac{x}{2} > \dfrac{3x}{4} + 2$

21 $\dfrac{x}{5} \leqslant \dfrac{x}{4} - 2$

Exercise 7.2H

1 Draw a pair of axes and label them 0 to 6 for both x and y.
   Show, by shading, the region where $x > 0$, $y > 0$ and $2x + 3y < 12$.

2 Draw a pair of axes and label them -2 to 2 for x and -4 to 8 for y.
   Show, by shading, the region where $x < 2$, $y > -2$ and $y < 3x + 2$.

3 Draw a pair of axes and label them 0 to 3 for x and 0 to 9 for y.
   Show, by shading, the region where $y < 6$, $y < 3x$ and $y > 2x$.

4 Draw a pair of axes and label them 0 to 8 for both x and y.
   Show, by shading, the region where $y > 0$, $y < x$ and $3x + 4y < 24$.

5 Draw a pair of axes and label them 0 to 8 for both x and y.
   Show, by shading, the region where $x > 0$, $8x + 3y < 24$ and $5x + 6y > 30$.

Chapter 8 Congruency

Exercise 8.1H

1 Triangles ABC and PQR are congruent.
  (a) Write down the size of angle
      (i) BAC   **(ii)** BCA
      (iii) PQR   **(iv)** RPQ

  (b) Which side in triangle PQR is 7.5 cm long?

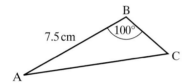
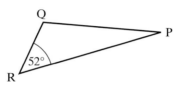

 2 Which triangles are congruent to triangle ABC?

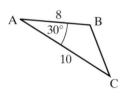
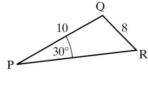
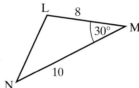
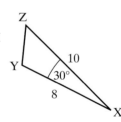

3 'SAS' is shorthand for 'Two sides and the included angle of one triangle are equal to the two sides and the included angle of the other triangle.'
Explain what each of these is shorthand for.
  (a) SSS   **(b)** ASA   **(c)** RHS

 4 State whether or not each of these pairs of triangles are congruent. Give reasons for your answers.

(a)
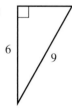

(b)
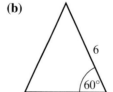

(c)
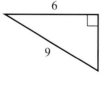

(d)
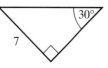
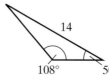
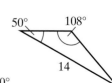

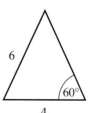

5 In the diagram, AB = BC and angle ABD = angle DBC.

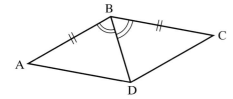

Prove that triangle ABD is congruent to triangle CBD.

 6 In the diagram, AB is parallel to ED and BC = CE.

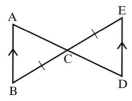

Prove that triangles ABC and DEC are congruent.

 7 (a) Sketch a quadrilateral ABCD in which angle ABC = angle ADC and BC is parallel to AD. Join the vertices A and C to make two triangles.
(You may recognise the shape you have drawn, but do not make any other assumptions about the shape except what you have been told.)

(b) Prove that triangles ABC and CDA are congruent.

(c) What does this prove about the opposite sides of the quadrilateral?

 8 (a) Sketch an isosceles triangle ABC with AB = AC.
Draw a straight line from the midpoint of BC to A.

(b) Use congruent triangles to prove that this line bisects the angle at A and is perpendicular to the side BC.

 9 (a) Sketch an equilateral triangle ABC. The midpoint of AB is X, the midpoint of BC is Y, and the midpoint of AC is Z.

(b) Prove that triangle XYZ is also equilateral.

 10 Two triangles have two sides of length 5 cm and 9 cm.
The angle opposite the 5 cm side is 25°.
The two triangles are not congruent.
Sketch the two triangles to show that they are not congruent.

Chapter 9 Simultaneous equations

Exercise 9.1H

Solve graphically each of these pairs of simultaneous equations.

1 $y = 3x$ and $y = 4x - 2$.
Use values of x from −1 to 4.

2 $y = 2x + 3$ and $y = 4x + 1$.
Use values of x from −2 to 3.

3 $y = x + 4$ and $4x + 3y = 12$.
Use values of x from −3 to 3.

4 $y = 2x + 8$ and $y = -2x$.
Use values of x from −5 to 1.

5 $2y = 3x + 6$ and $3x + 2y = 12$.
Use values of x from 0 to 4.

 6 Ted's Tool Hire charges £5 plus £8 a day to hire a chain saw.
Mike's Machine Hire charges £9 plus £7 a day to hire a chain saw.
 (a) Write an equation for the cost, £C, of hiring a chain saw for d days from
  (i) Ted's Tool Hire.
  (ii) Mike's Machine Hire.
 (b) On one graph draw the two lines of the equations connecting C and d, for values of d up to 5.
 (c) Use your graph to find the number of days for which the two companies charge the same amount.

Exercise 9.2H

Use algebra to solve each of these pairs of simultaneous equations.

1 $x + y = 3$
$2x + y = 4$

2 $2x + y = 6$
$2x - y = 2$

3 $2x - y = 7$
$3x + y = 13$

4 $2x + y = 12$
$x - y = 3$

5 $2x + y = 7$
$3x - y = 8$

6 $x + y = 4$
$3x - y = 8$

7 $x + 3y = 9$
$2x - 3y = 0$

8 $3x + y = 14$
$3x + 2y = 22$

9 $4x - y = 4$
$4x + 3y = 20$

10 $x - 4y = 2$
$x + 3y = 9$

Exercise 9.3H

Use algebra to solve each of these pairs of simultaneous equations.

1 $x + 3y = 5$
$2x + y = 5$

2 $2x - 5y = 3$
$x + y = 5$

3 $3x - y = 3$
$2x + 3y = 13$

4 $4x - y = 2$
$5x + 3y = 11$

5 $3x - 2y = 8$
$2x - y = 5$

6 $2x + y = 5$
$7x + 2y = 13$

7 $x + 3y = 4$
$3x + 2y = -2$

8 $4x + 3y = 11$
$x + 2y = 4$

9 $x + 2y = 8$
$2x - 3y = 9$

10 $x + y = 2$
$x + 3y = 5$

11 $3x - 2y = 19$
$x + 4y = -3$

12 $4x - 3y = 1$
$x + y = -5$

13 $3x + 2y = 4$
$x + 4y = 13$

14 $5x + y = 10$
$3x - 5y = 10$

15 $7x + 3y = 0$
$2x - 9y = 69$

16 $3x + 4y = 12$
$6x - 3y = 2$

17 $4x - 3y = 11$
$5x - y = 22$

 18 $3x + 4y = 19$
$5x + 3y = 17$

19 $3x - 2y = 13$
$7x + 6y = 9$

 20 $6x - 5y = -16$
$5x - 3y = -11$

21 Biscuits are sold in small and large packets.
Millie needs some biscuits for a coffee morning.
She works out that three small packets and one
large packet would give her 46 biscuits.
She also works out that one small packet and two
large packets would give her 42 biscuits.
Let the small packet contain *s* biscuits and the
large packet contain *b* biscuits.
   (a) Write down two equations in *s* and *b*.
   (b) Solve the equations to find how many
         biscuits are in each packet.

 22 Mr and Mrs Singh and their three children went
to a concert.
Their total entrance fee was £19.
Mrs Jones went to the same concert with two
other mothers and four children.
Their entrance fee was £27.
Let £*a* be the entrance fee for an adult and £*c* be
the entrance fee for a child.
   (a) Write down two equations in *a* and *c*.
   (b) Solve your equations to find the entrance fee
         for adults and children.

23 Bill buys some first-class and second-class stamps.
He buys *f* first-class stamps and *s* second-class
stamps.
Altogether he buys 13 stamps.
First-class stamps cost 41p each and second-class
stamps cost 32p each.
Altogether he spends £4.79.
   (a) Write down two equations in *f* and *s*.
   (b) Solve your equations to find how many of
         each type of stamps he buys.
         Hint: Take care with the units.

Exercise 10.1H

1 On squared paper, draw and label vectors to represent these column vectors.
Do not forget to put the arrows on.

$$\mathbf{a} = \begin{pmatrix} 3 \\ 6 \end{pmatrix}, \qquad \mathbf{b} = \begin{pmatrix} 5 \\ -2 \end{pmatrix}, \qquad \mathbf{c} = \begin{pmatrix} -4 \\ 1 \end{pmatrix},$$

$$\mathbf{d} = \begin{pmatrix} 0 \\ 3 \end{pmatrix}, \qquad \mathbf{e} = \begin{pmatrix} -4 \\ 0 \end{pmatrix}, \qquad \mathbf{f} = \begin{pmatrix} -5 \\ -3 \end{pmatrix}$$

2 Write down column vectors to represent these vectors.

(a) $\overrightarrow{AB}$ (b) $\overrightarrow{CB}$ (c) $\overrightarrow{BC}$

(d) $\overrightarrow{DC}$ (e) $\overrightarrow{DE}$ (f) $\overrightarrow{ED}$

(g) $\overrightarrow{AD}$ (h) $\overrightarrow{EA}$

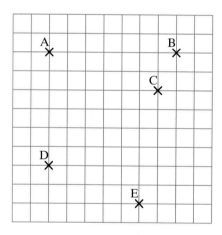

3 Find the column vector that maps the point
(a) (4, 3) on to (4, 7).
(b) (1, 3) on to (6, 7).
(c) (1, 7) on to (5, 1).
(d) (5, −2) on to (3, 6).
(e) (4, 7) on to (−1, 3).
(f) (7, −8) on to (−3, −3).

4 Write each of these vectors in terms of **a** and/or **b** as shown in the diagram.

(a) $\overrightarrow{AB}$ (b) $\overrightarrow{CD}$ (c) $\overrightarrow{EF}$

(d) $\overrightarrow{GH}$ (e) $\overrightarrow{IJ}$ (f) $\overrightarrow{KL}$

(g) $\overrightarrow{MN}$ (h) $\overrightarrow{PQ}$

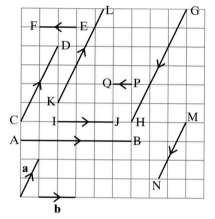

5 ABCDEF is a regular hexagon.
O is the centre of the hexagon.
$\overrightarrow{OA} = \mathbf{a}$ and $\overrightarrow{OB} = \mathbf{b}$

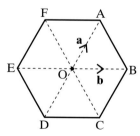

Write down each of these vectors in terms of **a** and/or **b**.

(a) $\overrightarrow{DC}$ (b) $\overrightarrow{DA}$ (c) $\overrightarrow{AF}$

(d) $\overrightarrow{BE}$ (e) $\overrightarrow{BC}$ (f) $\overrightarrow{AD}$

6 Copy and complete this table.

	Original point	Vector	New point
(a)	(1, 3)	$\begin{pmatrix} 2 \\ 5 \end{pmatrix}$	
(b)	(6, 1)	$\begin{pmatrix} -2 \\ 3 \end{pmatrix}$	
(c)	(8, 3)	$\begin{pmatrix} -5 \\ -3 \end{pmatrix}$	
(d)	(7, −2)	$\begin{pmatrix} -4 \\ 5 \end{pmatrix}$	
(e)	(−6, −1)	$\begin{pmatrix} -2 \\ 5 \end{pmatrix}$	
(f)	(−3, 6)	$\begin{pmatrix} -1 \\ -8 \end{pmatrix}$	

Exercise 10.2H

1 The diagram shows the vectors **a** and **b**.

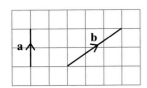

(a) Draw vectors **a** and **b** on squared paper.
(b) Draw vectors to represent each of these.
  (i) **a** + **b**   (ii) **b** − **a**
  (iii) 2**a** + **b**   (iv) 2**a** − **b**
  (v) **a** + $\frac{1}{2}$**b**

2 $\mathbf{a} = \begin{pmatrix} 3 \\ 5 \end{pmatrix}$, $\mathbf{b} = \begin{pmatrix} -1 \\ 4 \end{pmatrix}$ and $\mathbf{c} = \begin{pmatrix} 0 \\ 2 \end{pmatrix}$.

Work out these.
(a) **a** + **b**   (b) **a** − **b**
(c) 2**a** + 3**b**   (d) 2**a** − **c**
(e) **b** + 2**a** − $\frac{1}{2}$**c** (f) 2**a** − 3**b** + 5**c**

3 ABCD is a parallelogram.
E, F, G and H are the midpoints of the sides.
$\overrightarrow{AB} = \mathbf{p}$ and $\overrightarrow{AD} = \mathbf{q}$

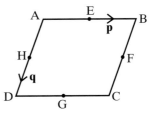

Find each of these vectors in terms of **p** and **q**.
(a) $\overrightarrow{AC}$ (b) $\overrightarrow{AF}$ (c) $\overrightarrow{ED}$
(d) $\overrightarrow{CE}$ (e) $\overrightarrow{FG}$

4 ABCD is a trapezium.
$\overrightarrow{AD} = \mathbf{p}$ and $\overrightarrow{AB} = \mathbf{q}$
$\overrightarrow{BC} = \frac{1}{2}\overrightarrow{AD}$

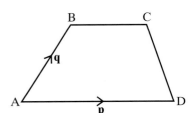

Find each of these vectors, as simply as possible, in terms of **p** and/or **q**.
(a) $\overrightarrow{BC}$ (b) $\overrightarrow{AC}$
(c) $\overrightarrow{BD}$ (d) $\overrightarrow{DC}$

5 In the diagram, P is two thirds of the way along AB.
$\overrightarrow{OA} = \mathbf{a}$ and $\overrightarrow{OB} = \mathbf{b}$

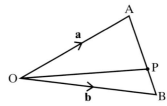

Find each of these vectors, as simply as possible, in terms of **a** and **b**.
(a) $\overrightarrow{BA}$ (b) $\overrightarrow{BP}$ (c) $\overrightarrow{OP}$

6 In the diagram, AOD and BOC are straight lines.
OD is three times as long as AO.
OC is three times as long as BO.

$\overrightarrow{OA} = \mathbf{a}$ and $\overrightarrow{OB} = \mathbf{b}$

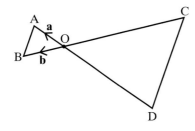

(a) Find each of these vectors in terms of **a** and **b**.

(i) $\overrightarrow{AB}$ (ii) $\overrightarrow{OD}$

(iii) $\overrightarrow{OC}$ (iv) $\overrightarrow{CD}$

(b) What two facts can you conclude about the lines AB and CD?

7 Write each of these vectors in terms of **a** and **b**.

(a) $\overrightarrow{AB}$ (b) $\overrightarrow{CD}$ (c) $\overrightarrow{EF}$

(d) $\overrightarrow{GH}$ (e) $\overrightarrow{IJ}$ (f) $\overrightarrow{KL}$

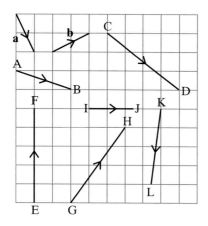

8 In the diagram, $\overrightarrow{OA} = \mathbf{a}$ and $\overrightarrow{OC} = \mathbf{c}$.
D is one third of the way along AC.

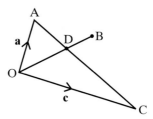

(a) Find each of these vectors, as simply as possible, in terms of **a** and **c**.

(i) $\overrightarrow{AC}$

(ii) $\overrightarrow{AD}$

(iii) $\overrightarrow{OD}$

(b) $\overrightarrow{OB} = \frac{3}{2}\overrightarrow{OD}$
Find each of these vectors, as simply as possible, in terms of **a** and **c**.

(i) $\overrightarrow{OB}$

(ii) $\overrightarrow{AB}$

(c) What two facts can you conclude about the lines AB and OC?

Circle theorems

Exercise 11.1H

In each of the questions, find the size of the angle or length marked with a letter.
Give a reason for each step of your work.

1

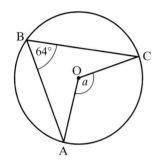

2

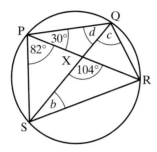

3

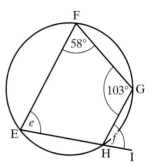

4

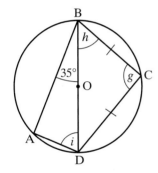

5

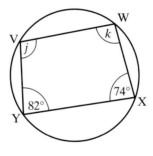

6

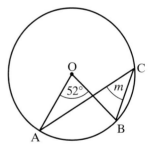

7

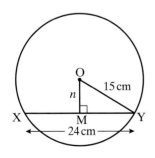

8

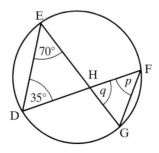

9

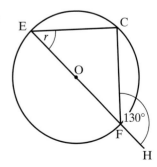

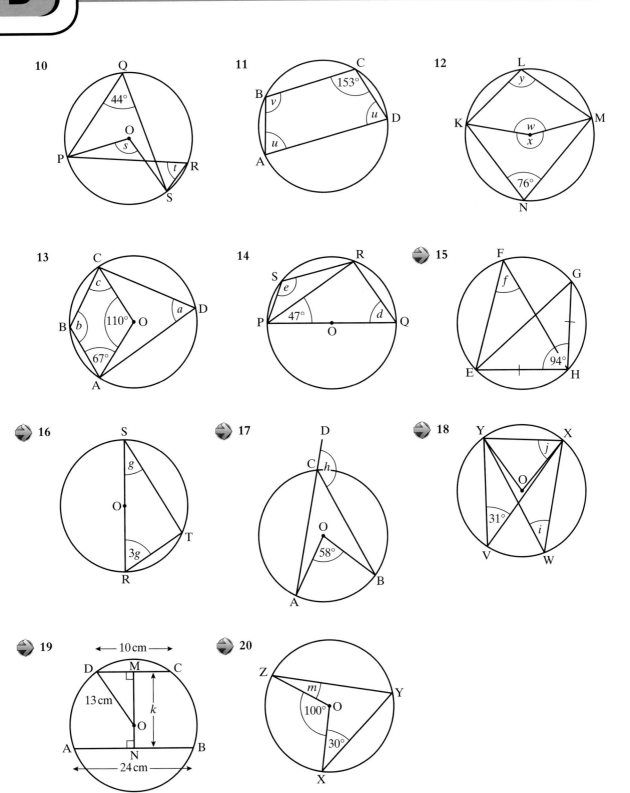

Exercise 11.2H

In each of the questions, find the size of the angles marked with letters.
Give a reason for each step of your work.

1

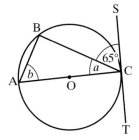

2

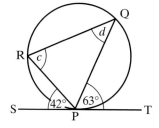

3

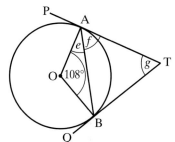

4

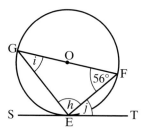

5

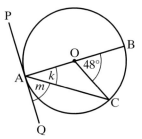

6

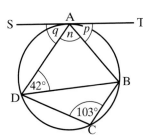

7

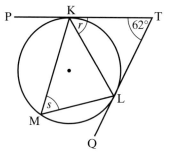

8

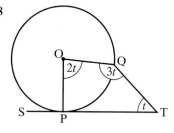

9

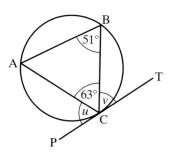

10

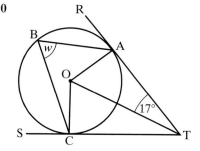

Chapter 12

Scatter diagrams and time series

Exercise 12.1H

1   Bill grows tomatoes. As an experiment he divided his land into eight plots.
    He used a different amount of fertiliser on each plot.
    The table shows the weight of tomatoes he got from each of the plots.

Amount of fertiliser (g/m²)	10	20	30	40	50	60	70	80
Weight of tomatoes (kg)	36	41	58	60	70	76	75	92

   (a) Draw a scatter diagram to show this information.
   (b) Describe the correlation shown in the scatter diagram.
   (c) Draw a line of best fit on your scatter diagram.
   (d) What weight of tomatoes should Bill expect to get if he uses 75 g/m² of fertiliser?

2   The table shows the prices and mileages of seven second–hand cars of the same model.

Price (£)	6000	3500	1000	8500	5500	3500	7000
Mileage	29 000	69 000	92 000	17 000	53 000	82 000	43 000

   (a) Draw a scatter diagram to show this information.
   (b) Describe the correlation shown in the scatter diagram.
   (c) Draw a line of best fit on your scatter diagram.
   (d) Use your line of best fit to estimate
       (i)   the price of this model of car which has covered 18 000 miles.
       (ii) the mileage of this model of car which costs £4000.

3   The heights of 10 daughters, all aged 20, and their fathers are given in the table below.

Height of father (cm)	167	168	169	171	172	172	174	175	176	182
Height of daughter (cm)	164	166	166	168	169	170	170	171	173	177

   (a) Draw a scatter diagram to show this information.
   (b) Describe the correlation shown in the scatter diagram.
   (c) Draw a line of best fit on your scatter diagram.
   (d) Use your line of best fit to estimate the height of a 20-year-old daughter whose father is 180 cm tall.

Exercise 12.2H

1 The table shows the number of people visiting a cinema complex each day for a 4-week period.

	Su	M	Tu	W	Th	F	Sa
Week 1	2135	1051	1604	2015	1752	1854	3045
Week 2	2614	1252	1527	1927	1813	1927	2984
Week 3	2542	1306	1614	1852	1782	2016	3257
Week 4	2968	1422	1827	2094	1905	2283	3371

(a) Plot a time-series graph of these figures.
(b) Calculate the 7-day moving averages and add these to the graph.
(c) Describe the trend.

2 The table shows the number of letters delivered by a postman each day for a 4-week period.

	M	Tu	W	Th	F	Sa
Week 1	201	205	304	196	316	92
Week 2	192	216	296	142	301	115
Week 3	185	205	310	185	298	106
Week 4	170	186	284	135	277	72

(a) Plot a time-series graph of these figures.
(b) Calculate the 6-day moving averages and add these to the graph.
(c) Describe the trend over this period.

3 These figures show the number of mobile text messages sent by the Peters' family over a period of 3 years.

	1st quarter	2nd quarter	3rd quarter	4th quarter
Year 1	210	192	361	242
Year 2	262	352	572	391
Year 3	354	529	834	682

(a) Describe the seasonal variation.
(b) Calculate the 4-point moving averages.
(c) Describe the trend.

4   The graph shows a shop's quarterly sales of ice-cream.

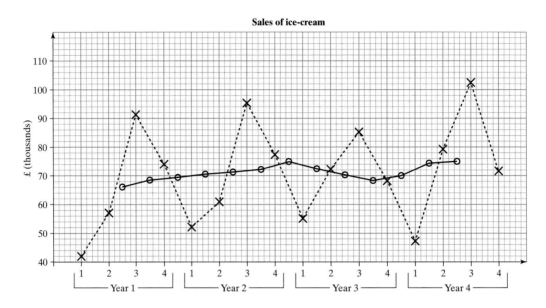

Sales of ice-cream

(a) Use readings from this graph to show how the third moving average has been calculated.
(b) Comment on the seasonal variation shown on the graph.
(c) Which summer had disappointing sales?

Unit C Contents

1	Algebraic manipulation	78
2	Perimeter, area, volume and 2-D representation	80
3	Trial and improvement	85
4	Probability 1	86
5	Graphs 1	89
6	Measures	97
7	Percentage and proportional change	101
8	Standard form and using a calculator	104
9	Similarity	107
10	Factorising	110
11	Three-dimensional geometry	112
12	Proportion and variation	115
13	Graphs 2	118
14	Quadratic equations	120
15	Simultaneous equations	123
16	Trigonometry	124
17	Functions	128
18	Length, area and volume	131
19	Probability 2	137
20	Algebraic fractions	140

Algebraic manipulation

Exercise 1.1H

Expand the brackets.

1 $(x + 1)(x + 2)$

2 $(x + 3)(x + 4)$

3 $(x + 2)(x - 1)$

4 $(x + 5)(x - 3)$

5 $(x - 1)(x - 2)$

6 $(x + 1)(x - 5)$

7 $(x + 3)(x - 3)$

8 $(x + 2)^2$

9 $(x - 7)^2$

10 $(x - 12)(x - 9)$

11 $(a + 5)(a + 3)$

12 $(b + 2)(b + 4)$

13 $(4 + c)(3 + c)$

14 $(p + 7)(p - 7)$

15 $(s - 6)(s - 1)$

16 $(t + 1)(t - 6)$

17 $(y + 3)(y + 2)$

18 $(x - 2)(x + 3)$

19 $(a - 9)^2$

20 $(p + 4)^2$

Exercise 1.2H

Expand and simplify these.

1 $(x - 4)(x - 5)$

2 $(x + 3)(x - 7)$

3 $(x - 8)(4x - 1)$

4 $(2x + 4)(3x + 2)$

5 $(3x + 5)(x - 2)$

6 $(4x + 3)(2x - 4)$

7 $(7x - 2)(2x - 7)$

8 $(3x - 5)(2x + 3)$

9 $(3x + 7)^2$

10 $(3a + 4b)(5a + 2b)$

11 $(2m - 3n)(3m + 2n)$

12 $(5p - 3q)(2p - q)$

13 $(a + 3b)(3a - 2b)$

14 $(3x - 4y)(2x + 3y)$

15 $(5a + 2b)(5a - 2b)$

16 $(2d + 3)(4d - 3)$

17 $(5e + 4)(3e - 2)$

18 $(3 + 8f)(2 - 5f)$

19 $(3g - 2)(5g - 6)$

20 $(4h - 5)(3h - 7)$

21 $(5j - 6)(3j - 8)$

22 $(3k + 7)(4k - 5)$

23 $(2 + 7m)(3 - 8m)$

24 $(4 + 3n)(2 - 5n)$

25 $(2 + 5p)(3 - 7p)$

26 $(5r - 6)(2r - 5)$

27 $(3s - 2)(4s - 9)$

Exercise 1.3H

1 Expand and simplify these.

(a) $\sqrt{2}\left(5 + \sqrt{2}\right)$ **(b)** $\sqrt{3}\left(\sqrt{12} + \sqrt{2}\right)$

(c) $4\sqrt{5}\left(2 + \sqrt{45}\right)$ **(d)** $3\sqrt{2}\left(\sqrt{18} + \sqrt{5}\right)$

2 Expand and simplify these.

(a) $\left(1 + 2\sqrt{7}\right)\left(3 + 4\sqrt{7}\right)$

(b) $\left(3 - \sqrt{3}\right)\left(8 + \sqrt{3}\right)$

(c) $\left(4 - \sqrt{5}\right)\left(3 - 2\sqrt{5}\right)$

(d) $\left(\sqrt{5} + 1\right)\left(\sqrt{5} - 4\right)$

(e) $\left(\sqrt{10} + 5\right)\left(\sqrt{10} - 5\right)$

(f) $\left(6 - \sqrt{13}\right)\left(4 - 2\sqrt{13}\right)$

3 Find the value of each of these expressions, when $m = 4 + \sqrt{5}$ and $n = 6 - 2\sqrt{5}$.

(a) $3n$ **(b)** $m + 2n$

(c) $3m - 2n$ **(d)** mn

4 Find the value of each of these expressions, when $p = 7 + 2\sqrt{3}$ and $q = 7 - 2\sqrt{3}$.

(a) $4p$ **(b)** $\sqrt{3}q$ **(c)** $p - q$

(d) pq **(e)** p^2 **(f)** q^2

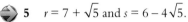 **5** $r = 7 + \sqrt{5}$ and $s = 6 - 4\sqrt{5}$.

(a) Find the value of k if $3r + ks$ is rational.

(b) Find the value of k if $3r + ks$ is of the form $a\sqrt{5}$.

Exercise 2.1H

Find the area of each of these triangles.

1
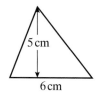
5 cm

6 cm

2
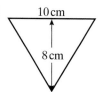
10 cm

8 cm

3
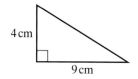
4 cm

9 cm

4
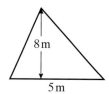
8 m

5 m

5
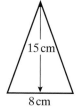
15 cm

8 cm

6
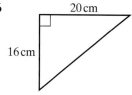
20 cm

16 cm

7
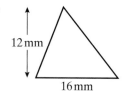
12 mm

16 mm

8
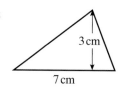
3 cm

7 cm

Exercise 2.2H

Find the area of each of these parallelograms.

1
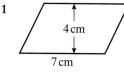
4 cm

7 cm

2

6 cm

9 cm

3

10 cm

2.5 cm

4
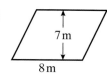
7 m

8 m

5
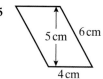
5 cm 6 cm

4 cm

6

4 cm

5.5 cm

7
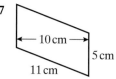
10 cm

5 cm

11 cm

8
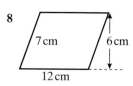
7 cm 6 cm

12 cm

Exercise 2.3H

Find the area of each of these shapes.
Break them down into rectangles and right–angled
triangles first.

1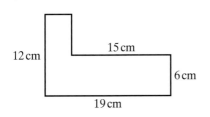

2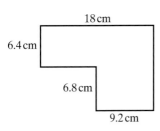

3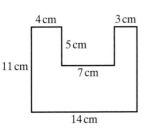

4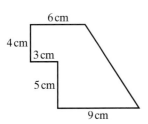

5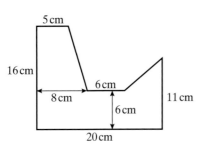

6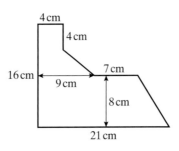

Exercise 2.4 H

1 Find the circumferences of the circles with these
   diameters.
   (a) 8 cm   (b) 17 cm   (c) 39.2 cm
   (d) 116 mm   (e) 5.1 m   (f) 6.32 m
   (g) 14 cm   (h) 23 cm   (i) 78 mm
   (j) 39 mm   (k) 4.4 m   (l) 2.75 m

2 Find the circumferences of the circles with these
   radii.
   (a) 3 cm   (b) 27 cm   (c) 68 mm
   (d) 49 m   (e) 0.9 m   (f) 2.65 m

3 Find the circumferences of the circles with these
   radii.
   Leave your answer in terms of π.
   (a) 5 cm   (b) 14 cm   (c) 33 mm
   (d) 8 m   (e) 2.5 m   (f) 30 m

4 A wheel of a car has a diameter of 52 cm.
   How many complete revolutions will the wheel
   complete in a journey of 2 kilometres?

5 A window in the shape of a semicircle is to be
   made with a metal frame round it.
   The diameter of the circle is 1.6 metres.
   Work out the length of metal needed to make
   the frame in terms of π.

Exercise 2.5H

1 Find the areas of the circles with the following radii.

(a) 17 cm	**(b)** 23 cm	**(c)** 67 cm
(d) 43 mm	**(e)** 74 mm	**(f)** 32 cm
(g) 58 cm	**(h)** 4.3 cm	**(i)** 8.7 cm
(j) 47 m	**(k)** 1.9 m	**(l)** 2.58 m

2 Find the areas of the circles with the following diameters.

(a) 18 cm	**(b)** 28 cm	**(c)** 68 cm
(d) 38 mm	**(e)** 78 mm	**(f)** 58 cm
(g) 46 cm	**(h)** 6.4 cm	**(i)** 7.6 cm
(j) 32 m	**(k)** 3.4 m	**(l)** 4.32 m

3 Find the area of the circles with these radii. Leave your answer in terms of π.

(a) 5 cm

(b) 14 cm

(c) 11 mm

(d) 7 m

4 A circular lawn has a radius of 12 metres. A circular flower bed of radius 3 metres has been cut out of the centre of the lawn. Find the remaining area of the lawn.

5 Tracey is making a gift tag. She punches a circular hole of diameter 4 mm out of a rectangular piece of card 60 mm by 40 mm. Find the area of card that is left in terms of π.

Exercise 2.6H

Find the volume of each of these shapes.

1
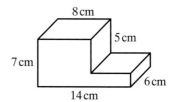

2
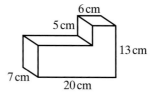

3
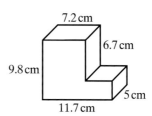

4
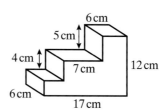

5
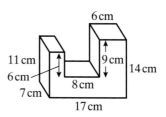

6
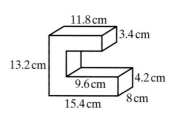

Exercise 2.7H

Find the volume of each of these prisms.

1

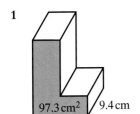

97.3 cm² 9.4 cm

2

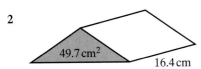

49.7 cm² 16.4 cm

3

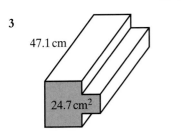

47.1 cm

24.7 cm²

4

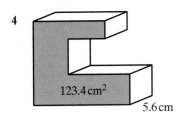

123.4 cm²

5.6 cm

5

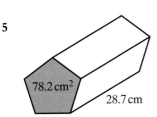

78.2 cm²

28.7 cm

6 39.7 cm

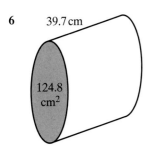

124.8 cm²

Exercise 2.8H

1 Find the volumes of the cylinders with these dimensions.
  (a) Radius 7 cm and height 29 cm
  (b) Radius 13 cm and height 27 cm
  (c) Radius 25 cm and height 80 cm
  (d) Radius 14 mm and height 35 mm
  (e) Radius 28 mm and height 8 mm
  (f) Radius 0.6 mm and height 5.1 mm
  (g) Radius 1.7 m and height 5 m
  (h) Radius 2.6 m and height 3.4 m

2 A cylindrical vase has a radius of 6 cm and a height of 20 cm.
  Find the volume of the vase in terms of π.

3 Tomatoes are grown in a poly-tunnel which has the shape of a half cylinder.
  The diameter of the end is 18 metres and the length is 50 metres.
  Calculate the volume of the tunnel.

Exercise 2.9H

1 Find the curved surface areas of cylinders with these dimensions.
  (a) Radius 9 cm and height 16 cm
  (b) Radius 13 cm and height 21 cm
  (c) Radius 27 cm and height 12 cm
  (d) Radius 17 mm and height 35 mm
  (e) Radius 12 mm and height 6 mm
  (f) Radius 3.7 mm and height 63 mm
  (g) Radius 1.9 m and height 19 m
  (h) Radius 2.7 m and height 4.3 m

2 A tin of beans has a diameter of 6.5 cm and a height of 12 cm.
  A label wraps round the whole curved surface of the tin.
  Find the area of the label.

3   Find the total surface areas of the closed cylinders
    with these dimensions.
    (a) Radius 8 cm and height 11 cm
    (b) Radius 17 cm and height 28 cm
    (c) Radius 29 cm and height 15 cm
    (d) Radius 32 mm and height 8 mm
    (e) Radius 35 mm and height 12 mm
    (f) Radius 3.9 mm and height 45 mm
    (g) Radius 0.8 m and height 7 m
    (h) Radius 2.9 m and height 1.7 m

4   Find the total surface area of a closed cylinder
    with a radius of 8 cm and a height of 4 cm.
    Give your answer in terms of π.

Exercise 2.10H

1   Draw the plan view, front elevation and side
    elevation of each of these objects.

    (a)

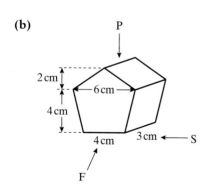

    (b)

(c)

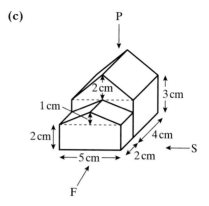

(d)

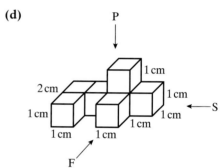

2   The two diagrams show a plan and a front
    elevation of a shape.
    Sketch the shape and draw a side elevation.

    Plan

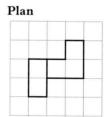

    Front elevation

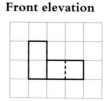

Chapter 3

Trial and improvement

Exercise 3.1H

1 Show that a solution of $x^3 - 2x - 1 = 0$ lies between 1 and 2.
Find this solution correct to 1 decimal place.

2 Show that a solution of $x^3 + 5x - 3 = 0$ lies between 0 and 1.
Find this solution correct to 1 decimal place.

3 Show that a solution of $x^3 - 5x + 2 = 0$ lies between −3 and −2.
Find this solution correct to 1 decimal place.

4 Show that the equation $x^3 - 5x + 2 = 0$ has another solution between 0 and 1.
Find this solution correct to 1 decimal place.

5 Find a solution, between $x = 2$ and $x = 3$, to the equation $x^3 = 11$.
Give your answer correct to 1 decimal place.

6 (a) Show that a solution to the equation
$x^3 + 3x = 30$ lies between $x = 2$ and $x = 3$.
(b) Find the solution correct to 1 decimal place.

7 (a) Show that a solution to the equation
$x^3 - 2x = 70$ lies between $x = 4$ and $x = 5$.
(b) Find the solution correct to 1 decimal place.

8 Find a solution to the equation $x^3 + 4x = 100$.
Give your answer correct to 1 decimal place.

9 Find a solution to the equation $x^3 + x = 60$.
Give your answer correct to 2 decimal places.

10 Find a solution to the equation $x^3 - x^2 = 40$.
Give your answer correct to 2 decimal places.

11 A number, x, added to the square of that number is equal to 1000.
(a) Write this as an equation.
(b) Find the number correct to 1 decimal place.

12 The cube of a number minus the number is equal to 600.
Find the number correct to 2 decimal places.

Probability 1

Exercise 4.1H

1 The probability that Stacey will go to bed late tonight is 0.2.
   What is the probability that Stacey will not go to bed late tonight?

2 The probability that I will throw a six with a dice is $\frac{1}{6}$.
   What is the probability that I will not throw a six?

3 The probability that it will snow on Christmas Day is 0.15.
   What is the probability that it will not snow on Christmas Day?

4 The probability that someone chosen at random is left-handed is $\frac{3}{10}$.
   What is the probability that they will be right-handed?

5 The probability that United will lose their next game is 0.08.
   What is the probability that United will not lose their next game?

6 The probability that Ian will eat crisps one day is $\frac{17}{31}$.
   What is the probability that he will not eat crisps?

Exercise 4.2H

1 A shop has brown, white and wholemeal bread for sale.
   The probability that someone will choose brown bread is 0.4 and the probability that they will choose white bread is 0.5.
   What is the probability of someone choosing wholemeal bread?

2 A football coach is choosing a striker for the next game.
   He has three players to choose from: Wayne, Michael and Alan.
   The probability that he will choose Wayne is $\frac{5}{19}$ and the probability that he will choose Michael is $\frac{7}{19}$.
   What is the probability that he will choose Alan?

3 A bag contains red, white and blue counters.
   Jill chooses a counter at random.
   The probability that she chooses a red counter is 0.4 and the probability that she chooses a blue counter is 0.15.
   What is the probability that she chooses a white counter?

4 Elaine goes to town by car, bus, taxi or bike.
   The probability that she uses her car is $\frac{12}{31}$, the probability that she catches the bus is $\frac{2}{31}$ and the probability that she takes a taxi is $\frac{13}{31}$.
   What is the probability that she rides her bike into town?

5 A biased five-sided spinner is numbered 1 to 5.
   The table shows the probability of obtaining some of the scores when it is spun.

Score	1	2	3	4	5
Probability	0.37	0.1	0.14		0.22

   What is the probability of getting a 4?

6 A cash bag contains only £20, £10 and £5 notes.
   One note is chosen from the bag at random.
   There is a probability of $\frac{3}{4}$ that it is a £5 note and a probability of $\frac{3}{20}$ that it is a £10 note.
   What is the probability that it is a £20 note?

Exercise 4.3H

1 The probability that United will lose their next game is 0.2.
How many games would you expect them to lose in a season of 40 games?

2 The probability that it will be rainy on any day in June is $\frac{2}{15}$.
On how many of June's 30 days would you expect it to be rainy?

3 The probability that an eighteen-year-old driver will have an accident is 0.15.
There are 80 eighteen-year-old drivers in a school.
How many of them might be expected to have an accident?

4 When Phil is playing chess, the probability that he wins is $\frac{17}{20}$.
In a competition, Phil plays 10 games.
How many of them might you expect him to win?

5 An ordinary six-sided dice is thrown 90 times.
How many times might you expect to get
(a) a 4? **(b)** an odd number?

6 A box contains twelve yellow balls, three blue balls and five green balls.
A ball is chosen at random and its colour noted. The ball is then replaced. This is done 400 times.
How many of each colour might you expect to get?

Exercise 4.4H

1 Pete rolls a dice 200 times and records the number of times each score appears.

Score	1	2	3	4	5	6
Number of times	29	34	35	32	34	36

(a) Work out the relative frequency of each of the scores. Give your answers to 2 decimal places.
(b) Do you think that Pete's dice is fair? Give a reason for your answer.

2 Rory kept a record of his favourite football team's results.
Win: 32   Draw: 11   Lose: 7

(a) Calculate the relative frequency of each of the three outcomes.
(b) Are your answers to part **(a)** good estimates of the probability of the outcome of their next match?
Give a reason for your answer.

3 In a survey, 600 people were asked which flavour
of crisps they preferred.
The results are shown in the table.
(a) Work out the relative frequency for each flavour.
Give your answers to 2 decimal places.
(b) Explain why it is reasonable to use these figures to
estimate the probability of the flavour of crisps
that the next person to be asked will prefer.

Flavour	Number of people
Plain	166
Salt and vinegar	130
Cheese and onion	228
Other	76

4 The owner of a petrol station notices that in one day 287 out of 340 people filling their car with petrol spent over £20.
Use these figures to estimate the probability that the next customer will spend
(a) over £20.   **(b)** £20 or less.

5 Jasmine made a spinner numbered 1, 2, 3, 4 and 5.
She tested the spinner to see if it was fair.
The table shows her results.

Score	1	2	3	4	5
Number of times	46	108	203	197	96

(a) Work out the relative frequency of each of the scores.
Give your answers to 2 decimal places.
(b) Do you think that the spinner is fair?
Give a reason for your answer.

6 A box contains yellow, green, white and blue counters.
A counter is chosen from the box and its colour noted.
The counter is then replaced in the box.
The table gives information about the colour of counter picked.

Colour	Relative frequency
Yellow	0.4
Green	0.3
White	0.225
Blue	0.075

(a) There are 80 counters altogether in the bag. How many do you think there are of each colour?
(b) What other information is needed before you can be sure that your answers to part **(a)** are accurate?

 7 While Jill is walking home from school she notices that eight of the 40 front doors she passes are painted red.
She says that therefore the probability that the next door will be painted red is $\frac{1}{5}$.
Explain why she is wrong.

8 William has three dice which he suspects may be biased.
(a) He throws the first dice 600 times and gets a six 92 times.
Is there evidence to suggest that this dice is biased? Give your reasons.
If there is, estimate the probability that the next throw is a six.
(b) He throws the second dice 600 times and gets a six 195 times.
Is there evidence to suggest that this dice is biased? Give your reasons.
If there is, estimate the probability that the next throw is a six.
(c) He throws the third dice 30 times and gets a six 9 times.
William says that this dice is biased.
Why do you think he came to this conclusion?

9 The table shows the results of a survey on the type of chocolate people prefer.

Type of chocolate	Number of people
Milk	382
Plain	145
White	99

Use these figures to estimate, correct to 2 decimal places, the probability that the next person surveyed will prefer
(a) milk chocolate.
(b) white chocolate.

5 Graphs 1

Exercise 5.1H

1   John and Imran live in the same block of flats and go to the same school.
   The graph represents their journeys home from school.

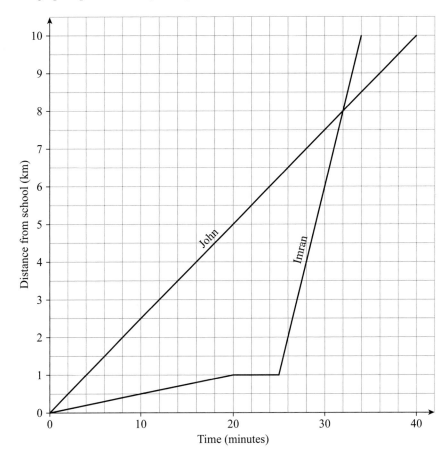

(a) Describe Imran's journey home.
(b) After how many minutes did Imran overtake John?
(c) How many minutes before John did Imran arrive home?
(d) Calculate John's speed in kilometres per minute.

2 The graph show the temperture on a certain day.

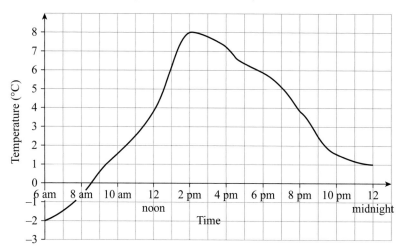

(a) At what time did the temperature first go above freezing point (0°C)?
(b) What was the maximum temperature?
(c) At what time was the temperature rising most quickly?
(d) For how many hours was the temperature above 6°C?

3 A model plane was launched.
It rose to a height of 25 metres in 30 seconds.
It climbed slowly at first and then faster.
It flew at a height of about 25 metres for 60 seconds.
It then dived to the ground in 5 seconds.
Draw a sketch to illustrate this story.

4 Simon had a bath. The graph shows the volume
(V gallons) of the water in the bath after t minutes.
(a) How many gallons of water are in the bath
at A?
(b) Simon got in the bath at B and out at F.
How long was he in the bath?
(c) Between O and A, the hot tap is on.
How many gallons of water per minute
came from the hot tap?
(d) Between A and B, both taps are on.
What is the rate of flow of both taps together?
Give your answer in gallons/minute.
(e) Describe what happened between C and E.
(f) At what rate did the bath empty?
Give your answer in gallons/minute.

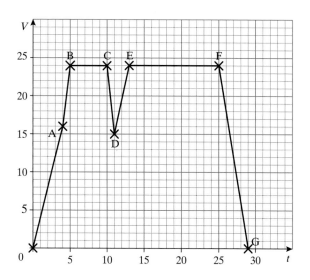

5 A printer's charge for printing programmes is worked out as follows.

A fixed charge of £a

+

x pence per programme for the first 1000 programmes

+

80 pence per programme for each programme over 1000

The graph below shows the total charge for printing up to 1000 programmes.

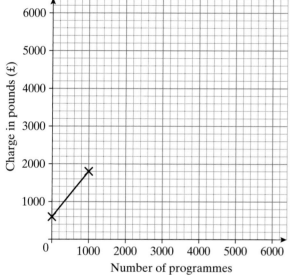

Charge in pounds (£) / Number of programmes

(a) What is the fixed charge, £a?
(b) Calculate x, the charge per programme for the first 1000 programmes.
(c) Copy the graph and add a line segment to show the charges for 1000 to 6000 programmes.
(d) What is the total charge for 3500 programmes?
(e) What is the average cost per programme for 3500 programmes?

 6 The graph shows a train journey.

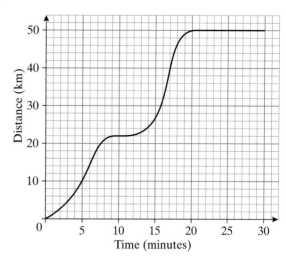

Distance (km) / Time (minutes)

(a) How long did the train journey take?
(b) How far was the train journey?
(c) How far from the start was the first station?
(d) How long did the train stop at the first station?
(e) When was the train travelling fastest?

 7 Water is poured into each of these vessels at a constant rate until they are full.

(a) **(b)**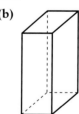

(c) 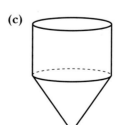 **(d)**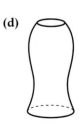

These graphs show the depth of water (*d*) against time (*t*).

Choose the most suitable graph for each vessel.

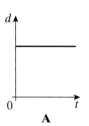

A

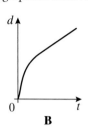

B

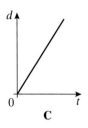

C

D

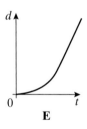

E

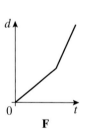

F

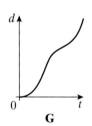

G

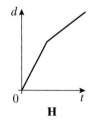

H

8 A mobile phone company offers its customers the choice of two price plans.

	Plan A	Plan B
Monthly subscription	£10.00	£*s*
Free talk time per month	60 minutes	100 minutes
Cost per minute over the free talk time	*a* pence	35 pence

The graph shows the charges for Plan A and the charges for Plan B up to 100 minutes.

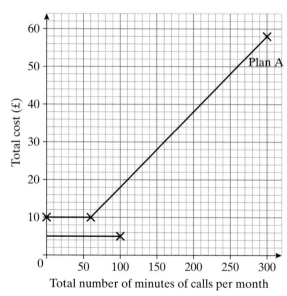

Total cost (£)

Total number of minutes of calls per month

(a) Find the monthly subscription for Plan B (£*s*).

(b) Shamir uses price plan B.
He uses the phone for 250 minutes per month.
How much does it cost?

(c) Copy the graph and add a line to show the charges for Plan B for 100 to 250 minutes.

(d) For how many minutes is the cost the same in both price plans?

(e) Which price plan is the cheaper when the time for calls is 220 minutes? By how much?

9   The table shows the cost of sending parcels.

Maximum weight	Cost
10 kg	£13.85
11 kg	£14.60
12 kg	£15.35
13 kg	£16.10
14 kg	£16.85
15 kg	£17.60

The graph shows the information in the first row in the table.

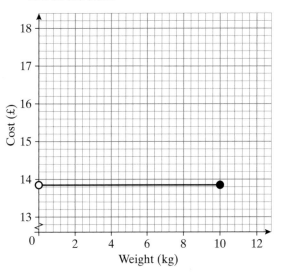

(a) What is the cost of sending a parcel weighing
   (i)   9.6 kg?
   (ii) 10 kg?
   (iii) 10.1 kg?
 (b) (i)   What is the meaning of the dot at the right of the line?
   (ii) What is the meaning of the circle at the left of the line?
(c) Copy the graph and extend the horizontal axis to 16 kg.
   Add lines to show the cost for parcels weighing up to 15 kg.
(d) Hazel posted one parcel weighing 8.4 kg and another weighing 12.8 kg.
   What was the total cost?

 10 15 000 people attended a football match.
   The gates opened 60 minutes before kick off.
   The match lasted 90 minutes with a break of 15 minutes at half-time.
   200 people left at half-time.
   Some people started leaving 10 minutes before the final whistle, but most stayed to the end.
   The grounds were cleared 30 minutes after the final whistle.
   Copy the axes below and sketch a graph of the number of people in the grounds against the time after the gates opened.

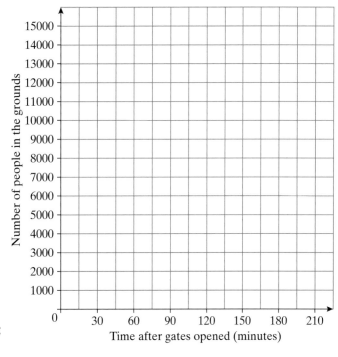

Exercise 5.2H

1 This is a distance–time graph for a particle moving in a straight line.

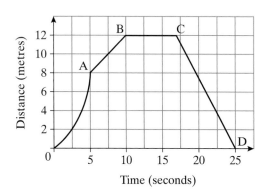

Describe the motion of the particle.

2 **(a)** Draw a distance–time graph with the Time axis (*t*) from 0 to 10 seconds and the Distance axis (*s*) from 0 to 20 metres. Draw a straight line joining (0, 0) to (8, 18).
(b) Calculate the velocity and describe the motion.

3 **(a)** Draw a velocity–time graph with the Time axis (*t*) from 0 to 10 seconds and the Velocity axis (*v*) from 0 to 20 m/s. Show a constant acceleration from $t = 0$, $v = 0$ to $t = 10$, $v = 15$.
(b) What is the velocity when $t = 6$?
(c) What is the acceleration?

4 A particle moves with a constant acceleration of 2 m/s² from $t = 0$ to $t = 3$.
It moves at a constant velocity for the next 5 seconds.
Then it moves with a constant acceleration of −1.25 m/s² for the next 12 seconds.
(a) Draw a velocity–time graph with the Time axis (*t*) from 0 to 20 seconds and the Velocity axis (*v*) from −10 to +10 m/s. Show the movement of the particle.
(b) What is the velocity from $t = 3$ to $t = 8$?
(c) When is the velocity zero?
(d) What is the velocity when $t = 20$?

5 This is a velocity–time graph to show the movement of a particle.

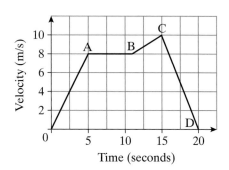

Describe as fully as possible the movement of the particle.
Work out the accelerations where necessary.

Exercise 5.3H

1 Which of these functions are quadratic?
For each of the functions that is quadratic, state whether the graph is U-shaped or ∩-shaped.
(a) $y = x^2 + 7$ **(b)** $y = 2x^3 + x^2 - 4$
(c) $y = x^2 + x - 7$ **(d)** $y = x(6 - x)$
(e) $y = \dfrac{5}{x^2}$ **(f)** $y = x(x^2 + 1)$
(g) $y = 2x(x + 2)$ **(h)** $y = 5 + 3x - x^2$

2 **(a)** Copy and complete the table of values for $y = 2x^2$.

x	−3	−2	−1	0	1	2	3
x^2	9					4	
$y = 2x^2$	18					8	

(b) Plot the graph of $y = 2x^2$.
Use a scale of 2 cm to 1 unit on the *x*-axis and 1 cm to 1 unit on the *y*-axis.
(c) Use your graph to
   (i) find the value of *y* when $x = -1.8$.
   (ii) solve $2x^2 = 12$.

3 (a) Copy and complete the table of values for $y = x^2 + x$.

x	−4	−3	−2	−1	0	1	2	3
x^2			4					9
$y = x^2 + x$								12

(b) Plot the graph of $y = x^2 + x$.
   Use a scale of 2 cm to 1 unit on the x-axis and 1 cm to 1 unit on the y-axis.
(c) Use your graph to
   (i)   find the value of y when $x = 1.6$.
   (ii) solve $x^2 + x = 8$.

4 (a) Copy and complete the table of values for $y = x^2 - x + 2$.

x	−3	−2	−1	0	1	2	3	4
x^2		4						16
$-x$		2						−4
2		2						2
$y = x^2 - x + 2$		8						14

(b) Plot the graph of $y = x^2 - x + 2$.
   Use a scale of 2 cm to 1 unit on the x-axis and 1 cm to 1 unit on the y-axis.
(c) Use your graph to
   (i)   find the value of y when $x = 0.7$
   (ii) solve $x^2 - x + 2 = 6$.

5 (a) Copy and complete the table of values for $y = x^2 + 2x - 5$.

x	−5	−4	−3	−2	−1	0	1	2	3
x^2				4					9
$2x$				−4					6
−5				−5					−5
$y = x^2 + 2x - 5$				−5					10

(b) Plot the graph of $y = x^2 + 2x - 5$.
   Use a scale of 2 cm to 1 unit on the x-axis and 1 cm to 1 unit on the y-axis.
(c) Use your graph to
   (i)   find the value of y when $x = -1.4$.
   (ii) solve $x^2 + 2x - 5 = 0$.

6 (a) Copy and complete the table of values for $y = 8 - x^2$.

x	-3	-2	-1	0	1	2	3
8				8			8
$-x^2$				0			-9
$y = 8 - x^2$				8			-1

(b) Plot the graph of $y = 8 - x^2$.
Use a scale of 2 cm to 1 unit on the x-axis and 1 cm to 1 unit on the y-axis.
(c) Use your graph to
   (i) find the value of y when $x = 0.5$.
   (ii) solve $8 - x^2 = -2$.

7 (a) Copy and complete the table of values for $y = (x - 2)(x + 1)$.

x	-3	-2	-1	0	1	2	3	4
$x - 2$		-4					1	
$x + 1$		-1					4	
$y = (x - 2)(x + 1)$		4					4	

(b) Plot the graph of $y = (x - 2)(x + 1)$.
Use a scale of 2 cm to 1 unit on the x-axis and 1 cm to 1 unit on the y-axis.
(c) Use your graph to
   (i) find the minimum value of y.
   (ii) solve $(x - 2)(x + 1) = 2.5$.

8 (a) Make a table of values for $y = x^2 - 3x + 2$.
Choose values of x from -2 to 5.
(b) Plot the graph of $y = x^2 - 3x + 2$.
Use a scale of 2 cm to 1 unit on the x-axis and 1 cm to 1 unit on the y-axis.
(c) Use your graph to solve
   (i) $x^2 - 3x + 2 = 1$.
   (ii) $x^2 - 3x + 2 = 10$.

Chapter 6 Measures

Exercise 6.1H

1 Change these units.
   (a) 25 cm to mm
   (b) 24 m to cm
   (c) 1.36 cm to mm
   (d) 15.1 cm to mm
   (e) 0.235 m to mm

2 Change these units.
   (a) $2 \, m^2$ to cm^2
   (b) $3 \, cm^2$ to mm^2
   (c) $1.12 \, m^2$ to cm^2
   (d) $0.05 \, cm^2$ to mm^2
   (e) $2 \, m^2$ to mm^2

3 Change these units.
   (a) $8000 \, mm^2$ to cm^2
   (b) $84\,000 \, mm^2$ to cm^2
   (c) $2\,000\,000 \, cm^2$ to m^2
   (d) $18\,000\,000 \, cm^2$ to m^2
   (e) $64\,000 \, cm^2$ to m^2

4 Change these units.
   (a) $32 \, cm^3$ to mm^3
   (b) $24 \, m^3$ to cm^3
   (c) $5.2 \, cm^3$ to mm^3
   (d) $0.42 \, m^3$ to cm^3
   (e) $0.02 \, cm^3$ to mm^3

5 Change these units.
   (a) $5\,200\,000 \, cm^3$ to m^3
   (b) $270\,000 \, mm^3$ to cm^3
   (c) $210 \, cm^3$ to m^3
   (d) $8.4 \, m^3$ to mm^3
   (e) $170 \, mm^3$ to cm^3

6 Change these units.
   (a) 36 litres to cm^3
   (b) 6300 ml to litres
   (c) 1.4 litres to ml
   (d) 61 ml to litres
   (e) $5400 \, cm^3$ to litres

7 A tile measures 34cm by 58cm and is 7mm thick. What is the volume of the tile?

Exercise 6.2H

1 Copy and complete each of these statements.
   (a) A length given as 4.3 cm, to 1 decimal place, is between .... cm and .... cm.
   (b) A capacity given as 463 ml, to the nearest millilitre, is between .... ml and .... ml.
   (c) A time given as 10.5 seconds, to the nearest tenth of a second, is between .... seconds and .... seconds.
   (d) A mass given as 78 kg, to the nearest kilogram, is between .... kg and .... kg.
   (e) An area given as $5.5 \, m^2$, to 1 decimal place, is between .... m^2 and .... m^2.

2 The number of people attending a football match was given as 24 000 to the nearest thousand. What was the least number of people that could have been at the match?

3 Kerry measures her height as 142 cm to the nearest centimetre.
   Write down the two values between which her height must lie.

4 The height of a desk is stated as 75.0 cm to 1 decimal place.
   Write down the two values between which its height must lie.

5 Rashid measures the thickness of a piece of plywood as 7.83 mm, to 2 decimal places.
   Write down the smallest and greatest thickness it could be.

6 The sides of this triangle are given in centimetres, correct to 1 decimal place.

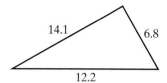

14.1   6.8

12.2

    (a) Write down the shortest and longest possible length of each side.
    (b) Write down the shortest and longest possible length of the perimeter.

 7 John has two pieces of string.
    He measures them as 125 mm and 182 mm, to the nearest millimetre.
    He puts the two pieces end to end.
    What is the shortest and longest that their combined lengths can be?

8 Mel and Mary both buy some apples. Mel buys 3.5 kg and Mary buys 4.2 kg.
    Both weights are correct to the nearest tenth of a kilogram.
    (a) What is the smallest possible difference between the amounts they have bought?
    (b) What is the largest possible difference between the amounts they have bought?

Exercise 6.3H

1 Rewrite each of these statements using sensible values for the measurements.
    (a) My mass is 78.32 kg
    (b) It takes Katriona 16 minutes and 15.6 seconds to walk to school.
    (c) The distance to London from Sheffield is 161.64 miles.
    (d) The length of our classroom is 5 metres 14 cm 3 mm.
    (e) My water jug hold 3.02 litres.

2 Give your answer to each of these questions to a sensible degree of accuracy.
    (a) Estimate the length of this line.

    (b) Estimate the size of this angle.

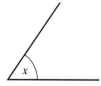

x

    (c) A rectangle is 2.3 cm long and 4.5 cm wide. Find the area of the rectangle.
    (d) The diameter of a circle is 8 cm. Work out the circumference.
    (e) The volume of a cube is 7 cm^3. Find the length of an edge.
    (f) An angle in a pie chart is found by working out $\frac{4}{7} \times 360°$. Find the angle.
    (g) A coach travels 73 miles at an average speed of 33 mph. How long does it take?
    (h) Six friends share £14 between them. How much does each one get?

Exercise 6.4H

1 A boat travels a distance of 24 km in 3 hours.
Calculate its average speed.

2 A car covers 197 miles on a motorway in 3 hours.
Calculate the average speed.
Give your answer to 1 decimal place.

3 Anne walks at an average speed of 3.5 km/h for
2 hours 30 minutes.
How far does she walk?

4 How long will it take a boat sailing at 12 km/h
to travel 64 km?

5 The density of a rock is 9.3 g/cm^3.
Its volume is 60 cm^3.
What is its mass?

6 Calculate the density of a piece of metal with a
mass of 300 g and a volume of 84 cm^3.
Give your answer to a sensible degree of accuracy.

7 A man walks 10 km in 2 hours 15 minutes.
What is his average speed in km/h?
Give your answer to a sensible degree of accuracy.

8 Calculate the mass of a stone of volume 46 cm^3
and density 7.6 g/cm^3.

9 Copper has a density of 8.9 g/cm^3.
Calculate the volume of a block of copper of
mass 38 g.
Give your answer to a sensible degree of accuracy.

10 What is the density of gas if a mass of 32 kg
occupies a volume of 25 m^3?
Give your answer to a sensible degree of accuracy.

11 A small town in America has a population of 235
and covers an area of 35 km^2.
Find the population density (number of people
per square kilometre) of the town.

12 A coach left the coach station at 09:10 and
travelled 72 km in 90 minutes, arriving at
Carter castle.
(a) Calculate its average speed.
The coach stopped at the castle for $3\frac{1}{2}$ hours
and then travelled back at an average speed of
55 km/h.
(b) What time did it arrive back at the coach
station?
Give your answer to the nearest minute.

13 Freeville has a population of 36 281 and its area
is 27.4 km^2.
Calculate its population density.
Give your answer to a sensible degree of accuracy.

14 A metal cylinder has a radius of 3.8 cm and a
height of 5.7 cm.
Its density is 12 g/cm^3.
Calculate its mass.

Exercise 6.5H

1 Find the upper and lower bounds for each of
these measurements.
(a) The height of a house is 8.5 m, to the nearest
0.1 m.
(b) A child weighs 57 kg to the nearest
kilogram.
(c) A door is 0.75 m wide to the nearest
centimetre.
(d) The winning time for the 100 m race was
12.95 seconds to the nearest hundredth of a
second.
(e) The volume of milk in a bottle is 500 ml to
the nearest millilitre.

2 A garden is measured as 43 m to the nearest metre.
Write the possible length of the garden as an
inequality.

3 A kitchen unit is 60 cm wide, to the nearest
centimetre.
(a) Is it possible that the unit will fit into a gap
60 cm wide, to the nearest centimetre?
Show how you decide.
(b) Is it certain that the unit will fit into the gap?
Show how you decide.

4 Find the upper and lower bounds for each of these measurements.
   (a) The total weight of 10 books, each book weighing 1.5 kg to the nearest 0.1 kg.
   (b) The total length of 20 paper clips, each measuring 3 cm to the nearest centimetre.
   (c) The total time to make 100 sandwiches when each sandwich takes 40 seconds to make, to the nearest second.

Exercise 6.6H

1 The lengths of the sides of a rectangle are 8 cm and 10 cm.
   Both measurements are correct to the nearest centimetre.
   Work out the upper and lower bounds of the perimeter of the rectangle.

2 Work out the largest and smallest possible areas of a triangle with a base of 7 cm and a height of 5 cm, where both lengths are to the nearest centimetre.

3 Sugar weighing 0.1 kg is taken from a bag weighing 2 kg.
   Both weights are correct to the nearest 0.1 kg.
   What are the maximum and minimum possible weights of the sugar remaining?

4 Two stages of a relay race are run in times of 14.07 seconds and 15.12 seconds, to the nearest 0.01 seconds.
   Calculate the upper bound of
   (a) the total time of the two stages.
   (b) the difference between the times for the two stages.

5 Given that $p = 5.1$ and $q = 8.6$, correct to 1 decimal place, work out the largest and smallest possible values of
   (a) $p \times q$.   (b) $q \div p$.

6 A train travels 150 miles in 1.8 hours.
   The distance is correct to the nearest mile and the time is correct to the nearest 0.1 hour.
   Work out the upper and lower bounds of the speed of the train.

7 The density of an object is given as 5.7 g/cm³ to the nearest 0.1 g/cm³.
   Its volume is 72.5 cm³ to 3 significant figures.
   Find the upper and lower bounds of the mass of the object.

   Scott is trying to work out a value for π.
   He measures the circumference of a circle as 32 cm and the diameter as 10 cm, both correct to the nearest centimetre.
   Calculate the upper and lower bounds of Scott's value for π.

9 Use the formula $a = \dfrac{v^2}{2s}$ to work out the upper and lower bounds of a when $v = 2.1$ and $s = 5.7$ and both values are correct to 1 decimal place.

10 Work out the upper and lower bounds of the following calculation.

$$\frac{9.4 - 5.2}{3.8}$$

   Each value in the calculation is correct to 2 significant figures.

11 Ann has a pencil 22.6 cm long.
   Could it fit into her pencil box which measures 22 cm by 5 cm?
   (All measurements are correct to the nearest millimetre.)

12 A water trough measures 150 cm by 40 cm by 55 cm, correct to the nearest centimetre.
   Could it hold 340 litres?

13 Don worked out that his average speed on the motorway is 58.3 mph (correct to 1 decimal place).
   He has a journey of 350 miles on motorways.
   Can he complete this in under 6 hours?

Percentage and proportional change

Exercise 7.1H

1   Wayne buys some potatoes at £1.25 a kilogram and six nectarines at 37p each.
    He gives the shop assistant £10 and gets £4.68 change.
    What weight of potatoes did he buy?

2   Chelsea, Sally and James share the profits from their business in the ratio 4 : 3 : 2.
    In 2009 the total profit was £94 500.
    Calculate how much Sally received.

3   Merry followed a recipe for lemon pudding which used 350 g of flour for four people.
    He made the recipe for 10 people and used a new 1.5 kg bag of flour.
    How much flour did he have left?

4   Mr Brown's mobile phone bill one month showed that he had used 53 minutes of calls at 13p per minute.
    His monthly rental charge was £15.30.
    There was VAT at 17.5% on the whole bill.
    Calculate the total bill including VAT.

5   In January 2008, the Retail Price Index (RPI) was 166.6.
    In January 2009 it was 171.1.
    Calculate the percentage increase in the RPI over that year.

6   In September 2007, the Average Earnings Index (AEI) was 113.9.
    During the next year it increased by 4.2%.
    Calculate the AEI in September 2008.

7   A water urn is in the shape of a cuboid, with the base a square of side 30 cm.
    How many litres of water does the urn contain when it is filled to a depth of 42 cm?

8   David drove 28 miles along the motorway at 70 mph and then 10 miles at 50 mph.
    (a) Calculate how long he took.
    (b) Find his average speed for the whole journey.

Exercise 7.2H

1   Graham invested £3500 at 4% compound interest.
    What was the investment worth at the end of 5 years?
    Give your answer to the nearest pound.

2   A car decreased in value by 11% per year.
    If it cost £16 500 new, what was it worth after 4 years?
    Give your answer to a sensible degree of accuracy.

3   In a certain country the population rose by 5% every year from 2003 to 2008.
    If the population was 26.5 million in 2003, what was the population in 2008?
    Give your answer in millions to the nearest 0.1 of a million.

4   Jane invested £4500 with compound interest for 3 years.
    She could receive either 3% interest every 6 months or 6% interest every year.
    Which should Jane choose?
    How much more will she receive?

5   Prices went up by 2% in 2007, 3% in 2008 and 2.5% in 2009.
    If an item cost £32 at the start of 2007 what would it cost at the end of 2009?

6   I invest £3000 at 3.5% compound interest.
    How many years must I leave it before its value exceeds £4000?

7 Ashlam is buying a sound system which he needs installing.
He sees these two adverts for the same sound system.

Sounds Rite
Cash
£1199 + VAT at 15%
Free Installation
Or Easy terms
Pay £500 deposit
+
12 monthly payments
of £85

Cheaper Sounds
Cash
£1350
Installation £40
Or Easy terms
20% deposit
+
12 monthly payments
of £99

Which company is cheaper for Ashlam and by how much if
(a) he is paying cash.
(b) he is paying by easy terms.

8 Jane has £5000 to invest.
She is looking at these two accounts.
They both pay compound interest annually.

Anglo Bank

No Notice Account

4.75%★★

★★Introductory
Offer
Reduces to 4.25%
after 1 year

Bonus Bank

No Notice
Account

4.5%

Find which bank pays the most interest over a three-year investment and by how much.

Exercise 7.3H

1 Calculate how much these items are worth if they increase by the given fraction each year for the given number of years.
Give your answers to the nearest penny.

	Original value	**Fractional increase**	**Number of years**
(a)	£5000	$\frac{1}{30}$	4
(b)	£300	$\frac{2}{7}$	3
(c)	£4500	$\frac{5}{9}$	6

2 Calculate how much these items are worth if they decrease by the given fraction each year for the given number of years.
Give your answers to the nearest penny.

	Original value	**Fractional decrease**	**Number of years**
(a)	£120	$\frac{1}{6}$	5
(b)	£5200	$\frac{3}{5}$	6
(c)	£140	$\frac{1}{2}$	4

3 Cathy invested £1870 with a bond that offered to increase the amount by $\frac{1}{12}$ each year.
How much was the bond worth after 4 years?

4 At Patnik shoe shop they offered to reduce the price of a pair of shoes by $\frac{1}{4}$ each day until they were sold.
They were priced at £47 to start with.
What was the price after four reductions?
Give your answer to the nearest penny.

5 It is estimated that the royalties from a book will decrease by $\frac{2}{5}$ each year.
In 2009 Kath received £11 000 in royalties.
If the estimate is correct, how much will she receive 5 years later?

Exercise 7.4H

1   Copy and complete this table.

	Original value	Percentage increase	Increased value
(a)	£750	8%	
(b)		15%	£414
(c)	£42.50	4.5%	
(d)		5%	£254

2   Copy and complete this table.

	Original value	Percentage decrease	Decreased value
(a)	£2000	12%	
(b)		5%	£240
(c)	£260	3.5%	
(d)		12.5%	£325

3   After an increase of 12%, a quantity is 84 tonnes.
What was it before the increase?

4   A newspaper increased its circulation by 3% and the new number sold was 58 195.
What was the circulation before the increase?

5   Santos bought a car for £14 750.
He sold it three years later at a loss of 45%.
What price did he sell it for?

6   A charity's income has been reduced by 2.5%.
Its income is now £8580.
What was it before the reduction?

7   It was announced that the number of people unemployed had decreased by 3%.
The number unemployed before the decrease was 2.56 million.
How many are now unemployed?

8   The price of a car is £12 925, including VAT at 17.5%.
What is the price without VAT?

9   At Percival's sale the price of everything was reduced by 7.5%, rounded to the nearest penny.
   (a) A pair of boots cost £94.99 before the sale.
      What was the price in the sale?
   (b) Delia was charged £13.87 for a blouse in the sale.
      What was its original price?

10 John's pension has increased by 4.75% and is now £924.56 a month.
What was it before the increase?

11 At St Bede's church they give $\frac{1}{8}$ of their weekly collection to overseas aid.
One week, they had £151.20 left after they had given away the money.
How much was the total collection?

12 The makers of Steamer's jam say that the new size jar contains a fifth more jam than the old size jar.
The new size jar contains 570 g.
How much did the old size jar contain?

13 One year the rate of Value Added Tax (VAT) went up from 17.5% to 20%.
Find the new cost of a computer that, before the increase, cost £752.

Chapter 8

Standard form and using a calculator

Exercise 8.1H

1 Write these numbers in standard form.
   (a) 60 000   (b) 8400
   (c) 863 000   (d) 72 500 000
   (e) 9 020 000   (f) 78
   (g) 5.2 million

2 Write these numbers in standard form.
   (a) 0.08   (b) 0.0096
   (c) 0.000 308   (d) 0.000 063
   (e) 0.000 004 8   (f) 0.000 000 023

3 These numbers are in standard form.
   Write them as ordinary numbers.
   (a) 3×10^3 (b) 4.6×10^4
   (c) 2×10^{-5} (d) 7.2×10^5
   (e) 1.9×10^{-4} (f) 5.78×10^6
   (g) 2.87×10^8 (h) 5.13×10^{-6}
   (i) 2.07×10^{-3} (j) 7.28×10^7

4 Write these numbers in order, smallest first.
   3.6×10^{-3}, 3.06×10^{-2}, 6.3×10^{-3}, 3.06×10^{-3}

Exercise 8.2H

1 Work out these without using your calculator.
   Give your answers in standard form.
   (a) $(6 \times 10^4) \times (3 \times 10^5)$
   (b) $(8 \times 10^6) \div (4 \times 10^3)$
   (c) $(9 \times 10^5) \times (4 \times 10^{-2})$
   (d) $(3 \times 10^{-3}) \times (2 \times 10^{-4})$
   (e) $(2 \times 10^8) \div (5 \times 10^3)$
   (f) $(7.6 \times 10^5) + (3.8 \times 10^4)$
   (g) $(5.6 \times 10^{-3}) - (4 \times 10^{-4})$

2 Work out these.
   Give your answers in standard form.
   (a) $(4.4 \times 10^6) \times (2.7 \times 10^5)$
   (b) $(6.5 \times 10^6) \times (2.3 \times 10^2)$
   (c) $(7.1 \times 10^4) \times (8.3 \times 10^2)$
   (d) $(2.82 \times 10^4) \div (1.2 \times 10^{-2})$
   (e) $(7.2 \times 10^3) \times (1.3 \times 10^5)$
   (f) $(4.3 \times 10^3) + (6.72 \times 10^4)$
   (g) $(6.21 \times 10^5) - (3.75 \times 10^4)$

3 By rounding the numbers to 1 significant
   figure and converting to standard form, find
   which of these is the most likely answer to
   $378\,000 \times 21\,600$.
   (a) 816 480 000   (b) 8 164 800 000
   (c) 81 648 000   (d) 81 648 000 000

4 $9.16 \times 4.8 = 43.968$
   Using this answer and by rounding the numbers
   to 1 significant figure and converting to standard
   form, find the answer to each of these
   calculations.
   (a) $9160 \times 48\,000$
   (b) $0.0916 \times 0.000\,48$
   (c) $916 \times 0.000\,048$

5 In 2005 the population of England was
   5.04×10^7, the population of Wales was
   2.96×10^6 and the population of Scotland
   was 5.09×10^6.
   (a) Work out the total population of England,
   Scotland and Wales.
   Give your answer in standard form.
   (b) The area of Scotland is 7.85×10^4 square
   kilometres.
   Work out the population density of Scotland
   in people per square kilometre.

Exercise 8.3H

Use your calculator to work out these.
Give all your answers to 3 significant figures.

1 (a) $\dfrac{1}{1.7} + \dfrac{1}{1.653}$

(b) $\dfrac{1}{0.9} \times \dfrac{1}{8.24}$

(c) $\dfrac{8.06}{5.91} - \dfrac{1.594}{1.62}$

2 (a) 0.741^3
(b) 2.28^{-5}
(c) $(9.2 + 15.3)^2$

3 (a) $\sqrt[4]{12.2}$

(b) $\sqrt[3]{0.8145 - 0.757}$

(c) $\sqrt[5]{8.6^2} + 9.71^3$

4 (a) $\sin 14.6°$
(b) $\tan 71.3°$
(c) $\sin 247° - \cos(-31)°$

5 (a) $\cos^{-1} 0.141$
(b) $\sin^{-1} 0.464$

(c) $\tan^{-1} \dfrac{1}{\sqrt{2}}$

6 (a) $(1.2 \times 10^4) \times (5.3 \times 10^6)$

(b) $\dfrac{4.06 \times 10^{-2}}{7 \times 10^{-4}}$

(c) $(5.9 \times 10^{-3}) \times (2.4 \times 10^{20})$

7 (a) $\dfrac{9.71 \times 0.0084765}{5.9^2}$

(b) $\dfrac{81.7 + 1.52}{62.8}$

(c) $\dfrac{9.61}{17.37 \times 224}$

8 (a) $\dfrac{101}{27.4 + 296}$

(b) $\dfrac{3.14 \times 0.782}{22.4 - 15.5}$

(c) $\dfrac{18.21 - 5.63}{23.48 + 19.76}$

9 (a) $3 \cos 12° - 5 \sin 12°$

(b) $\dfrac{3.4 \times \sin 47.1°}{\sin 19.2°}$

(c) $2.7^2 + 3.6^2 - 2 \times 2.7 \times 3.6 \cos 25°$

10 (a) $(3.6 \times 10^{-8})^2$

(b) $\sqrt{4.84 \times 10^6}$

(c) $\dfrac{(4.06 \times 10^6) + (1.15 \times 10^3)}{5.83 \times 10^{-6}}$

Exercise 8.4H

1 £30 000 is invested at 18% compound interest.
  (a) Write down a formula for the amount, a, the investment is worth after t years.
  (b) Calculate the value of the investment after
    (i) 5 years.
    (ii) 12 years.

2 The value of a currency, the scud, depreciates by 6% each month.
  I have 250 000 scuds.
  (a) Write down a formula for the value of the currency, c, after t months.
  (b) Calculate the value of 250 000 scuds after
    (i) 4 months.
    (ii) 9 months.
  (c) Use trial and improvement to work out how many months it will be before the 250 000 scuds are only worth as much as 100 000 scuds.

3 The population of a rare species of animal is decaying exponentially following the formula
  $$N = 60\,000 \times 2^{-t}$$
  where N is the number of these animals present and t is the time in years.
  (a) How many of these animals were there when the survey started?
  (b) How many of these animals were there after
    (i) 3 years?
    (ii) 10 years?
  (c) After how many years will this species of animal no longer exist; that is, after how many years will the number fall below 2?

4 Liz's employer tells her that her weekly wage will increase by a fixed percentage each year.
They tell her that the formula they will use is

$$A = 500 \times 1.04^n.$$

(a) How much is Liz's current weekly wage?
(b) What is the rate of increase?
(c) What does the letter n stand for in the formula?
(d) How much will her wage be after
  (i) 4 years?
  (ii) 10 years?

 5 The population of a country is increasing at a rate of 3% per year.
In 2009 the population was 38 million.
(a) Write down a formula for the population size, P, after t years.
(b) What will be the population in
  (i) 2014?
  (ii) 2104?
(c) How long will it take for the population to double from its 2009 size?

6 A sample of a radioactive element has a mass of 1 kg.
Its mass reduces by 10% each year.
(a) Write down a formula for the mass, m, of the element after t years.
(b) Calculate the mass after
  (i) 4 years.
  (ii) 8 years.
(c) Use trial and improvement to find how long it takes for the mass to halve.

Exercise 9.1H

1 These two rectangles are similar.
Calculate the length marked *x*.

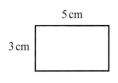
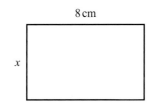

2 State, with reasons, which of these rectangles are similar.

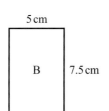

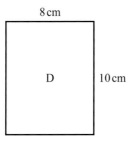

3 These two parallelograms are similar.
Calculate the length marked *x*.

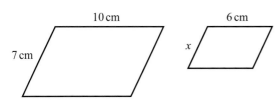

4 The triangles PQR and STU are similar.
Calculate the lengths of ST and SU.

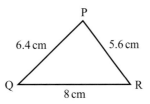
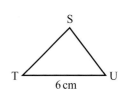

5 The triangles ABC and DEF are similar.
Calculate the lengths of AB and EF.

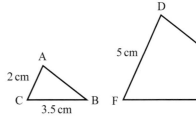

6 In the diagram, BC is parallel to DE.
AB = 5.6 cm, AC = 7.2 cm,
BC = 4.6 cm and DE = 6.9 cm.

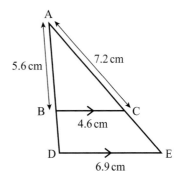

(a) Explain why triangle ABC is similar to triangle ADE.
(b) Calculate the lengths of BD and CE.

7 Explain why these trapeziums are not similar.

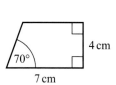

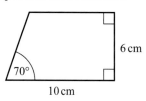

8 Look at these two triangles.

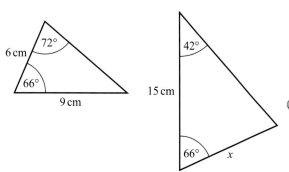

(a) Explain why the triangles are similar.
(b) Calculate the length of the side marked x.

9 The quadrilaterals ABCD and PQRS are similar.

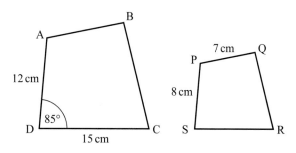

(a) Write down the size of angle PSR.
(b) Calculate the lengths of AB and SR.

10 A 5 m telegraph pole casts a shadow of 4.3 m.
At the same time a tree casts a shadow of 7.9 m.
Calculate the height of the tree.

11 In the diagram, PQ and TS are parallel.

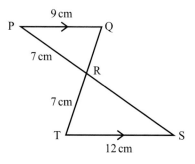

(a) Explain how you know that the two
triangles in the diagram are similar.
(b) Calculate the lengths RS and QR.

12 In the diagram, angle ABC = angle BCD = 90°,
AD = 3.1 cm and BD = 4.2 cm.

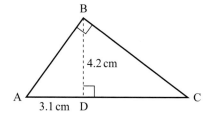

(a) Explain why triangles ABD and BCD are
similar.
(b) Calculate the length DC.
Give your answer correct to 3 significant
figures.

Exercise 9.2H

1 State the area scale factor for each of these linear
scale factors.
(a) 8   **(b)** 15

2 State the volume scale factor for each of these
linear scale factors.
(a) 6   **(b)** 20

3 State the linear scale factor for each of these.
(a) An area scale factor of 36
(b) A volume scale factor of 8

4 An oval mirror has an area of $162 \, cm^2$.
What is the area of a similar mirror one and a
half times as long?

5 The three tables in a nesting set of tables are similar, with heights in the ratio $1 : 1.2 : 1.5$. The area of the smallest table top is $120\,cm^2$. What is the area of the middle-sized table top?

6 A model of a theatre set is made to a scale of $1 : 20$.
A cupboard on the model has a volume of $50\,cm^3$. Find the volume of the cupboard on the actual set, giving your answer in m^3.

7 Two jugs are similar with capacities of 1 litre and 2 litres respectively.
The height of the larger jug is $14.8\,cm$.
What is the height of the smaller jug, to the nearest millimetre?

8 Julia is making a model of a wooden statue. She uses the same kind of wood as the original. The model is on a scale of $1 : 20$.
(a) The statue is $15\,m$ high.
How high will Julia's model be?
(b) 500 litres of varnish were needed for the statue.
How many litres will be needed for the model?
(c) Julia's model weighs $3\,kg$.
Estimate the weight of the statue.

9 Lego and Duplo are type of building bricks for children. Duplo bricks are designed for younger children and are twice as large as Lego bricks.

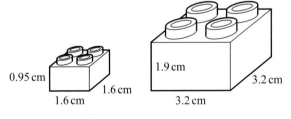

(a) Janet makes a shape using Duplo bricks. Her shape is $9.5\,cm$ high.
Elaine makes a similar shape from Lego. How high is Elaine's shape?
(b) The area of the base of Elaine's shape is $64\,cm^2$.
What is the area of the base of Janet's shape?
(c) The volume of Elaine's shape is $304\,cm^3$. What is the volume of Janet's shape?

10 This is a set of Russian dolls.

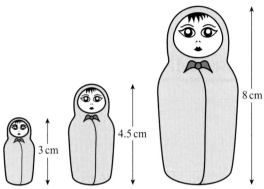

The larger dolls are enlargements of the smallest doll. The heights of the dolls are $3\,cm$, $4.5\,cm$ and $8\,cm$ respectively.
(a) The width of the smallest doll is $1.2\,cm$. What is the width of the largest doll?
(b) The surface area of the middle-sized doll is $8.4\,cm^2$.
What is the surface area of the smallest doll?
(c) The volume of the smallest doll is $4.2\,cm^3$. What is the volume of the middle-sized doll?

11 Shirley has a poster made from a photo. The poster is an enlargement of the photo with linear scale factor 8.
The dimensions of the photo are $5\,cm$ by $7\,cm$. What is the area of the poster?

12 A vase is $12\,cm$ tall.
Another similar vase is $18\,cm$ tall.
The larger vase has a capacity of $54\,cm^3$. What is the capacity of the smaller vase?

13 Two cuboids are similar.
The smaller cuboid has edges $4\,cm$, $5\,cm$ and $8\,cm$ long.
The larger one has a volume of $20\,000\,cm^3$. What is the length of the shortest edge of the larger cuboid?

14 A large tumbler is $16\,cm$ tall.
How tall is a similar tumbler that holds half as much?

15 A circle is enlarged by increasing the radius by 20%.
The radius was originally $12\,cm$.
What is the area of the enlarged circle?

Chapter 10 Factorising

Exercise 10.1H

Simplify each of these algebraic fractions.

1. $\dfrac{7x - 14}{4x + 8}$

2. $\dfrac{3x - 6}{9 - 12x}$

3. $\dfrac{12 + 8x}{6x - 4}$

4. $\dfrac{18 - 6x}{12 + 9x}$

5. $\dfrac{4x^2 + 2x}{2x^2 - 6x}$

6. $\dfrac{3x^2 - 4x}{5x^2 - 6x}$

7. $\dfrac{8 - 6x}{4x^2 + 6x}$

8. $\dfrac{3x^2 + 6x}{9x - 12x^2}$

Exercise 10.2H

Factorise each of these expressions.

1. $x^2 - 9$
2. $x^2 - 64$
3. $x^2 - 196$
4. $x^2 - y^2$
5. $25 - y^2$
6. $16 - c^2$
7. $a^2 - 10000$
8. $81 - s^2$
9. $x^2 - 36$
10. $49 - y^2$
11. $9x^2 - 25$
12. $4y^2 - 9$
13. $1 - 64t^2$
14. $x^2 - 121y^2$
15. $81a^2 - 16b^2$
16. $36a^2 - 25b^2$
17. $100 - 49y^2$
18. $2x^2 - 50y^2$
19. $3x^2 - 192$
20. $12x^2 - 75$

Exercise 10.3H

Factorise each of these expressions.

1. $x^2 + 4x + 3$
2. $x^2 + 5x + 4$
3. $x^2 + 7x + 12$
4. $x^2 - 2x + 1$
5. $x^2 - 5x + 4$
6. $x^2 - 12x + 20$
7. $x^2 + 21x + 20$
8. $x^2 - 16x + 28$
9. $x^2 + 10x + 9$
10. $x^2 + 6x + 9$
11. $x^2 + 9x + 20$
12. $x^2 + 14x + 24$
13. $a^2 - 9a + 8$
14. $b^2 - 3b + 2$
15. $a^2 - 10a + 16$
16. $s^2 - 14s + 24$
17. $y^2 - 11y + 30$
18. $y^2 + 13y + 30$
19. $x^2 - 17x + 16$
20. $c^2 - 18c + 32$

Exercise 10.4H

Factorise each of these expressions.

1. $x^2 + 2x - 15$
2. $x^2 - 3x - 28$
3. $x^2 + 6x - 7$
4. $x^2 - x - 12$
5. $x^2 - 5x - 14$
6. $x^2 - 9x - 10$
7. $x^2 + 5x - 36$
8. $x^2 - 9x - 36$
9. $x^2 + 9x - 10$
10. $a^2 + 2a - 8$
11. $a^2 + 4a - 12$
12. $y^2 - 2y - 15$
13. $b^2 + 5b - 24$
14. $a^2 + 2a - 24$
15. $c^2 - 5c - 36$
16. $x^2 - 12x - 28$
17. $x^2 + 13x - 14$
18. $y^2 + 2y - 48$
19. $a^2 - 4a - 21$
20. $x^2 + 21x - 100$

Exercise 10.5H

Factorise each of these expressions.

1 $x^2 + 8x + 12$

2 $2x^2 + 7x + 3$

3 $2x^2 - 5x + 2$

4 $6x^2 - 7x + 2$

5 $4x^2 - 8x + 3$

6 $4x^2 + 13x + 10$

7 $4x^2 + 21x + 5$

8 $3x^2 + 16x + 5$

9 $5x^2 - 16x + 3$

10 $6x^2 - 19x + 15$

11 $5x^2 + 23x + 12$

12 $2x^2 - 15x + 18$

13 $6x^2 + 13x + 6$

14 $10x^2 - 27x + 5$

15 $30x^2 - 11x + 1$

Exercise 10.6H

Factorise each of these expressions.

1 $x^2 - x - 12$

2 $2x^2 - 5x - 3$

3 $2x^2 - 5x - 12$

4 $3x^2 + 8x - 3$

5 $6x^2 + x - 1$

6 $4x^2 - 4x - 3$

7 $8x^2 - 2x - 3$

8 $6x^2 - 5x - 1$

9 $6x^2 - 7x - 10$

10 $10x^2 + 13x - 3$

11 $5x^2 - 23x - 10$

12 $4x^2 + x - 3$

13 $3x^2 - 2x - 8$

14 $6x^2 + x - 2$

15 $8x^2 - 18x - 5$

Exercise 10.7H

Simplify each of these expressions.

1 $\dfrac{20a^2b^3}{5b} \times \dfrac{b^3}{2a}$

2 $\dfrac{2x^2y}{6y^2} \times \dfrac{3y^2x}{2x^2}$

3 $\dfrac{7x}{x^2 - 5x}$

4 $\dfrac{2x^2 - 6x}{x^2 - x - 6}$

5 $\dfrac{x^2 + 2x - 3}{x^2 + 8x + 15}$

6 $\dfrac{x^2 + 2x - 8}{x^3 - 2x^2}$

7 $\dfrac{x^2 - 7x + 12}{x^2 - 9}$

8 $\dfrac{x^2 - 5x}{2x^2 - 11x + 5}$

9 $\dfrac{3x^2 + 14x - 5}{x^2 + 7x + 10}$

10 $\dfrac{9x^2 - 4}{3x^2 - x - 2}$

11 $\dfrac{3(x - 4)^2}{4x^2 - 64}$

12 $\dfrac{3x^2 + 14x + 8}{6x^2 - 5x - 6}$

Exercise 11.1H

1 OABCDEFG is a cuboid.
   F is the point (5, 7, 3).

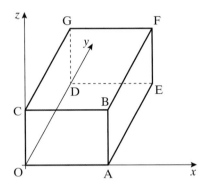

Write down the coordinates of
(a) point A.   (b) point B.
(c) point C.   (d) point D.
(e) point E.   (f) point G.

2 OABCV is a pyramid with a rectangular base.
   V is directly above the centre of the base, N.
   OA = 8 units, AB = 10 units and
   VN = 7 units.

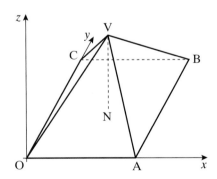

Write down the coordinates of
(a) point A.   (b) point B.
(c) point C.   (d) point N.
(e) point V.

3 OABCDEFG is a cuboid.
   M is the midpoint of BF and N is the midpoint
   of GF.
   OA = 6 units, OC = 5 units and
   OD = 3 units.

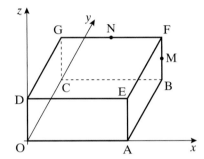

(a) Write down the coordinates of
    (i)   point B.
    (ii)   point F.
    (iii) point G.
    (iv)   point M.
    (v)   point N.
(b) (i)   The point $(6, 2\frac{1}{2}, 0)$ is the midpoint of
           which edge?
    (ii)   The point $(0, 2\frac{1}{2}, 1\frac{1}{2})$ is the centre of
           which face?

Exercise 11.2H

1 Calculate the distance between the points
   (4, −3, 7) and (−7, −6, 2).

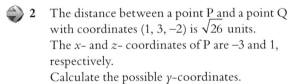 2 The distance between a point P and a point Q
   with coordinates (1, 3, −2) is $\sqrt{26}$ units.
   The x- and z- coordinates of P are −3 and 1,
   respectively.
   Calculate the possible y-coordinates.

3 A pyramid is 8 cm high and has a square base of
   side 6 cm.
   Its sloping edges are all of equal length.
   Calculate the length of a sloping edge.

4 The length of each sloping edge of a square-based pyramid is 12 cm.
The sides of the base are each 10 cm.
Calculate the height of the pyramid.

5 ABCDEF is a triangular wedge.
The faces ABFE, BCDF and ACDE are rectangles.

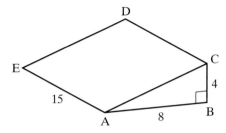

(a) Calculate the length AD.
(b) Calculate angle DAC.

6 The pyramid OABCD has a horizontal rectangular base ABCD as shown.
O is vertically above A.

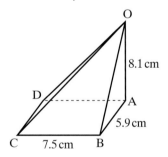

Calculate
(a) the length of OB.
(b) angle OCB.
(c) the length of OC.

7 The points A, B and C are in the same horizontal plane.
The angle of elevation of a vertical mast MC from A is 24.7°.
AC is 34 m and BC is 57 m.

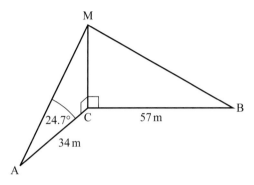

Find the angle of elevation of M from B.

8 A hot air balloon is flying at a height of 550 metres, having travelled 2 kilometres south and 3.5 kilometres west of its launch point.
Calculate its straight-line distance from the launch point.

9 Ted uses a box 32 cm by 13 cm by 11 cm to keep some tools in.
He buys a screwdriver which is 36 cm long and doesn't think it will fit in the box.
Show whether he is correct or not.

Exercise 11.3H

1 A square-based pyramid has sloping edges of length 9.5 cm.
The sloping edges make an angle of 60° with the base.
Calculate the height of the pyramid.

2 A pyramid is 7 cm high and has a square base of side 5 cm.
Its sloping edges are all of equal length.
Calculate the angle between a sloping face and the base.

3 In this cuboid, AB = 12 cm, BC = 5 cm and CG = 6 cm.

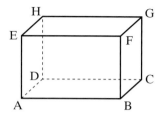

Calculate
(a) the length of AC.
(b) the length of AG.
(c) the angle between AG and AC.
(d) the angle between AG and face BCGF.

4 The length of the diagonal of a cuboid is 9.3 cm. The height of the cuboid is 5.6 cm. Calculate the angle between the diagonal and a vertical edge of the cuboid.

5 VABCD is a square-based pyramid of height 8 cm. Its base ABCD has side 10 cm. All its sloping edges are equal in length. M is the midpoint of AB.

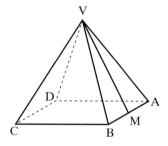

Calculate
(a) the angle which VM makes with the base.
(b) the length of VM.
(c) the length of VA.
(d) the angle which VA makes with the base.

6 VABCD is a square-based pyramid of height 8 cm. Its base ABCD has side 10 cm. V is directly above A.

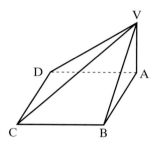

Calculate the lengths of the sloping edges VB, VC and VD, and the angles they make with the base.

7 This 'lean-to' workshop is a prism with a trapezium as its cross-section.

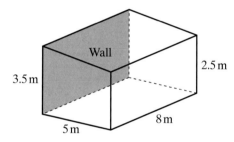

(a) Calculate the area of the sloping roof.
(b) Calculate the angle between the roof and the wall against which the workshop is built.
(c) Calculate the length of the longest piece of wood that will fit in the workshop.

8 The diagonal of a cuboid has length 12.4 cm. It makes an angle of 33° with the base of the cuboid.
(a) Calculate the height of the cuboid.
(b) The length of the base of the cuboid is 5.8 cm. Calculate its width.

Chapter 12

Proportion and variation

Exercise 12.1H

1 A carousel revolves 14 times in 252 seconds. How many revolutions does the carousel make in 90 seconds?

2 An express train travels 63 miles in 35 minutes. How long would it take the train to travel 45 miles at the same speed?

3 Sound can travel 5145 metres in 15 seconds. How far can sound travel in 24 seconds?

4 A piece of wax with a volume of 240 cm³ has a mass of 216 grams.
What is the mass of 1000 cm³ of wax?

5 Tiling a floor with an area of 15 m² uses 21 litres of adhesive.
How much adhesive would be needed to tile a floor with an area of 35 m²?

6 A 45 minute telephone call costs £1.80. How much does it cost to make a 12 minute call at the same rate?

7 A contractor is paid £75 for working 6 hours. How much would the contractor be paid for working 10 hours at the same rate?

8 A machine cleans a carpet with an area of 12 m² using 21 litres of water.
How much water would the machine use to clean a similar carpet with an area of 40 m²?

9 An aeroplane travels 54 km in 6 minutes. How far would it travel in 15 minutes at the same speed?

10 A person can walk 340 metres in 4 minutes. How far would the same person walk in 3 minutes?

Exercise 12.2H

1 A journey takes 30 minutes at a constant speed of 40 miles per hour. How long would the journey take at a constant speed of 60 miles per hour?

2 It takes a team of 12 men 10 weeks to lay a pipeline. How long would the pipeline take to lay if there were 15 men?

3 A pool can be emptied in 18 hours using four pumps. How long would it take to empty the pool using three pumps?

4 A supply of hay is enough to feed eight horses for 30 days. For how long would the same supply feed 20 horses?

5 Using three ploughs it is possible to plough a field in 6 hours. How long would it take to plough the same field using two ploughs?

6 It takes a team of three men 14 hours to install a fence. How long would it take to install the fence if there were eight men?

7 A tank can be filled using three pumps in a period of 28 hours. How long would it take to fill the tank using seven pumps?

8 A carpet with an area of 16 m² costs £440. What is the cost of 26 m² of the same carpet?

9 A supply of corn is enough to feed 24 pigs for 35 days. For how long would the same supply of corn feed 60 pigs?

10 An express train completes a journey of 473 miles in 5.5 hours. How long would it take the train to travel 129 miles at the same speed?

Exercise 12.3H

1 For each of these relationships
    (i)   state the type of proportion.
    (ii)   find the formula.
    (iii) find the missing y value in the table.

(a)

x	1	8	15
y	6	48	

(b)

x	4	12	18
y	36	12	

(c)

x	4	10	36
y	2	12.5	

(d)

x	3	4	5
y	8	4.5	

(e)

x	2	5	20
y	30	12	

(f)

x	4	60	100
y	5	75	

(g)

x	4	7	40
y	35	20	

(h)

x	2	3	6
y	9	4	

(i)

x	1	4	10
y	10	160	

(j)

x	3	15	75
y	15	75	

(k)

x	3	4	10
y	24	18	

(l)

x	2	5	32
y	8	50	

(m)

x	12	60	150
y	4	20	

(n)

x	5	10	20
y	8	2	

2 Boyle's law states that the pressure of a gas, P Pascals, varies inversely with its volume, $V\,\text{m}^3$, at constant temperature.
    (a) If $P = 10$ Pascals when $V = 100\,\text{m}^3$, find the formula.
    (b) Find P when $V = 500\,\text{m}^3$.

Exercise 12.4H

1 For each of these relationships
   (i) state the type of proportion.
   (ii) find the formula.

(a)
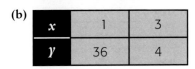

x	2	6
y	8	72

(b)

x	1	3
y	36	4

(c)
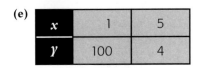

x	5	12
y	8.64	1.5

(d)

x	6	10
y	9	25

(e)

x	1	5
y	100	4

2 The gravitational force, F, between a satellite and the Earth is inversely proportional to the square of its distance, d, from the centre of the Earth.

The rule can be written as $F \propto \dfrac{1}{d^2}$.

(a) The radius of the Earth is 6400 km.
So, at 12 800 km above the Earth's surface d is three times its value on the Earth's surface. What is the effect on the force of gravity at this height?

(b) How far above the Earth's surface is the satellite when the gravitational force is one quarter that on the Earth's surface?

3 As part of their training, astronauts have to experience the effects of large accelerations, called 'G forces'.
The training consists of being placed in a pod at the end of a rotor arm which is spun at speed. The force experienced, F, is proportional to the square of the speed, s, of the pod.
This relationship can be written as $F \propto s^2$.
When the pod is spinning with a speed of 6 m/s the force experienced is 2G.
How many Gs will be experienced when the speed is 18 m/s?

Chapter 13 — Graphs 2

Exercise 13.1H

1 (a) Draw the graph of $y = x^2 - 3x + 2$ for values of x from -1 to 4.
   (b) On the same axes, draw the line $y = x - 1$.
   (c) Write down the coordinates of the points where the line and the curve intersect.

2 (a) Draw the graph of $y = x^2 - 2x - 3$ for values of x from -2 to 4.
   (b) On the same axes, draw the line $y = 3 - x$.
   (c) Write down the coordinates of the points where the line and the curve intersect.

3 (a) Draw the graph of $y = x^2 - 6x + 4$ for values of x from 0 to 6.
   (b) On the same axes, draw the line $4y = 3x - 12$.
   (c) Write down the coordinates of the points where the line and the curve intersect.

4 (a) Draw the graph of $y = 10 + x - 2x^2$ for values of x from -3 to 3.
   (b) On the same axes, draw the line $3y + 4x = 12$.
   (c) Write down the coordinates of the points where the line and the curve intersect.

Exercise 13.2H

1 (a) Draw the graph of $y = x^2 - 5x - 6$ for values of x from -2 to 7.
   (b) Use your graph to solve these equations.
      (i) $x^2 - 5x - 6 = 0$
      (ii) $x^2 - 5x - 6 = -10$
      (iii) $x^2 - 5x - 6 = 2 - 3x$

2 (a) Draw the graph of $y = x^2 - 4x + 3$ for values of x from -1 to 5.
   (b) Use your graph to solve these equations. Give your answers to 1 decimal place.
      (i) $x^2 - 4x + 3 = 0$
      (ii) $x^2 - 4x - 3 = 0$
      (iii) $x^2 - 6x + 7 = 0$

 3 (a) Draw the graph of $y = x^2 + 2x - 15$ for values of x from -6 to 4.
   (b) Use your graph to solve these equations. Give your answers to 1 decimal place.
      (i) $x^2 + 2x - 15 = 0$
      (ii) $x^2 + 2x - 10 = 0$
      (iii) $x^2 + 3x - 4 = 0$
   (c) (i) What line would you need to draw on the graph to solve the equation $x^2 + x + 3 = 0$?
       (ii) Why does this not work?

For the remaining questions, do not draw the graphs.

 4 The graph of $y = x^2 - 2x + 1$ has been drawn. What other line needs to be drawn to solve each of these equations?
   (a) $x^2 - 2x + 1 = 5$
   (b) $x^2 - 2x + 1 = 3x - 2$

 5 The graph of $y = x^2 - x - 12$ has been drawn. What other line needs to be drawn to solve each of these equations?
   (a) $x^2 - 3x - 12 = 0$
   (b) $x^2 - x = 0$
   (c) $x^2 + x - 15 = 0$

 6 The graph of $y = x^2 - 6x + 8$ has been drawn. What other line needs to be drawn to solve each of these equations?
   (a) $x^2 - 6x + 4 = 0$
   (b) $x^2 - 8x + 8 = 0$
   (c) $x^2 - 4x + 3 = 0$

Exercise 13.3H

1 **(a)** Copy and complete this table of values for the equation $y = \dfrac{12}{x}$.

x	1	2	3	4	6	8	12
y							

(b) Draw the graph of $y = \dfrac{12}{x}$ for values of x between 1 and 12.

(c) Use your graph to estimate the value of y when $x = 9$.

(d) (i) Find the point on the graph where $x = y$.

  (ii) Explain the connection of this number with 12.

2 **(a)** Draw the graph of $y = 2x^3$ for values of x between −3 and 3.

(b) Draw the line $y = 10x$ on the same graph.

(c) (i) Find the equation that is given at the intersection of the line and the curve.

  (ii) Estimate the solutions to this equation.

3 **(a)** Draw the graph of $y = \dfrac{6}{x + 1}$, for values of x between 0 and 5.

(b) Use your graph to find the value of x when $y = 4$.

(c) Draw the line $y = x − 1$ on the same graph.

(d) (i) Find the equation that is given at the intersection of the line and the curve.

  (ii) Estimate the solutions to this equation.

4 **(a)** Draw a graph of $y = 4^{-x}$ for values of x between −2 and 2.

(b) Use your graph to estimate
  (i) the value of y when $x = 0.5$.
  (ii) the solution to the equation $4^{-x} = 10$.

5 The table shows two pairs of values for the equation $y = ab^x$.

x	0	1	2	3	4	5
y	4	8				

(a) Find the values of a and b.

(b) Copy and complete the table.

(c) Draw the graph of $y = ab^x$ for values of x from 0 to 5.

(d) Use your graph to estimate the value of x when $y = 80$.

6 A car, which cost £10000 when new, depreciates in value by 10% each year.
The formula for finding the value, £v, after t years is $v = 10\,000 \times (0.9)^t$.

(a) Copy and complete this table of values.

Age in years (t)	Value (£v)
0	
1	
2	
3	
4	

(b) Draw the graph of v against t.

(c) Use your graph to estimate the age of the car when its value had dropped to £7000.

(d) Use your graph to estimate when the car's value had dropped to 75% of its original cost.

14 Quadratic equations

Exercise 14.1H

Solve each of these quadratic equations.

1 $x(x + 3) = 0$

2 $x(x - 4) = 0$

3 $(x - 2)(x + 2) = 0$

4 $(x - 5)(x + 6) = 0$

5 $3x(x + 5) = 0$

6 $(x + 10)(x - 1) = 0$

7 $(x - 7)(x - 3) = 0$

8 $(x + 9)(2x - 5) = 0$

9 $(x - 3)(4x - 1) = 0$

10 $(3x - 7)(2x + 1) = 0$

11 $4x(3x - 2) = 0$

12 $(2x - 3)(3x - 4) = 0$

Exercise 14.2H

Solve each of these quadratic equations.

1 $x^2 + 5x + 4 = 0$

2 $x^2 - 8x + 7 = 0$

3 $x^2 + 4x - 5 = 0$

4 $x^2 - x - 2 = 0$

5 $x^2 + x - 12 = 0$

6 $x^2 + 7x = 0$

7 $x^2 - 9x + 14 = 0$

8 $x^2 - 3x - 10 = 0$

9 $3x^2 - 15x = 0$

10 $x^2 - 16 = 0$

11 $x^2 + 8x + 12 = 0$

12 $x^2 - 8x - 20 = 0$

13 $x^2 + 8x + 16 = 0$

14 $x^2 - 8x + 15 = 0$

15 $x^2 - 100 = 0$

16 $x^2 + 21x - 22 = 0$

17 $2x^2 - 6x = 0$

18 $x^2 - 11x + 18 = 0$

19 $4x^2 + 2x = 0$

20 $9x^2 - 25 = 0$

21 $2x^2 + 3x + 1 = 0$

22 $3x^2 - 5x + 2 = 0$

23 $3x^2 + 10x + 7 = 0$

24 $2x^2 + 5x - 3 = 0$

25 $3x^2 + 4x - 4 = 0$

26 $2x^2 - 17x + 8 = 0$

27 $4x^2 - 4x + 1 = 0$

28 $4x^2 - 11x - 3 = 0$

29 $2x^2 - x - 10 = 0$

30 $6x^2 - 7x - 5 = 0$

Exercise 14.3H

Solve each of these quadratic equations.

1 $x^2 + x = 6$

2 $x^2 = 7x - 10$

3 $x^2 = 4x + 5$

4 $x^2 = 10x - 21$

5 $x^2 = 11x$

6 $x^2 = 12 - 4x$

7 $x^2 = 6 + 5x$

8 $2x^2 = 3x - 1$

9 $9 + 8x - x^2 = 0$

10 $5 - 4x - x^2 = 0$

11 I think of a number. I subtract 2 from it.
I multiply the result by the original number and
subtract 3. The answer is 45.
Write down an equation and solve it to find the
original number.

12 A rectangle has a width of x cm and its length is
3 cm longer than its width.
(a) Write down the length of the rectangle in
terms of x.
(b) The area of the rectangle is 54 cm^2.
Write an equation in x and show that it
simplifies to $x^2 + 3x - 54 = 0$.
(c) Solve your equation to find the length and
width of the rectangle.

Exercise 14.4H

1 **(a)** Write each of these quadratic expressions in
the form $(x + m)^2 + n$.
(i) $x^2 + 2x$ **(ii)** $x^2 - 4x$
(iii) $x^2 - 14x$ **(iv)** $x^2 - x$
(b) Write each of these quadratic expressions in
the form $(x + m)^2 + n$.
Use your answers to part **(a)**.
(i) $x^2 + 2x - 5$ **(ii)** $x^2 - 4x + 7$
(iii) $x^2 - 14x + 1$ **(iv)** $x^2 - x - 7$

2 For each of these quadratic expressions, complete
the square; that is, write it in the form $(x + m)^2 + n$.
(a) $x^2 + 6x - 1$
(b) $x^2 + 8x - 2$
(c) $x^2 - 4x + 3$
(d) $x^2 - 2x - 3$
(e) $x^2 - 12x + 37$
(f) $x^2 + 10x - 3$
(g) $x^2 - 6x + 19$
(h) $x^2 + 3x - 2$
(i) $x^2 - 5x + 7$

Exercise 14.5H

In this exercise, give all your answers correct to
2 decimal places.

1 Solve each of these quadratic equations.
(a) $(x - 2)^2 - 5 = 0$
(b) $(x + 3)^2 - 7 = 0$
(c) $(x - 4)^2 - 20 = 0$
(d) $(x + 1)^2 - 11 = 0$

2 For each of these quadratic equations, first
complete the square and then solve the equation.
(a) $x^2 - 6x - 5 = 0$
(b) $x^2 + 4x + 1 = 0$
(c) $x^2 - 4x - 3 = 0$
(d) $x^2 + 10x + 5 = 0$
(e) $x^2 + 2x - 8 = 0$
(f) $x^2 + 6x - 2 = 0$
(g) $x^2 - 8x + 6 = 0$
(h) $x^2 + 14x - 3 = 0$
(i) $x^2 + 3x - 6 = 0$

Exercise 14.6H

Solve each of these quadratic equations using the formula.
Give your answers correct to 2 decimal places.
If there are no real solutions, say so.

1 $x^2 + 3x + 1 = 0$

2 $x^2 - 7x + 3 = 0$

3 $x^2 + 2x - 11 = 0$

4 $x^2 + x - 7 = 0$

5 $2x^2 + 6x + 3 = 0$

6 $2x^2 + 5x + 1 = 0$

7 $x^2 + 4x + 7 = 0$

8 $3x^2 + 10x + 5 = 0$

9 $3x^2 - 7x - 4 = 0$

10 $2x^2 - x - 8 = 0$

11 $5x^2 + 8x + 1 = 0$

12 $2x^2 + 5x - 7 = 0$

13 $4x^2 - 12x + 6 = 0$

14 $2x^2 - 5x - 4 = 0$

15 $2x^2 + 10x + 15 = 0$

16 $3x^2 + 3x - 2 = 0$

17 $x^2 - 3x - 50 = 0$

18 $4x^2 + 9x + 3 = 05$

19 $5x^2 + 11x + 4 = 0$

20 $3x^2 - x - 8 = 0$

21 $2x^2 + 6x + 5 = 0$

 22 The area of a rectangle is 70 cm².
The width of the rectangle is x cm, and its length is 4 cm longer than its width.
Form an equation and solve it to find the dimensions of the rectangle, giving your answers in centimetres correct to 2 decimal places.

Simultaneous equations

Exercise 15.1H

Solve each of these pairs of simultaneous equations by substitution.

1   $y = 2x - 10$
    $y = 3x - 13$

2   $y = 5x + 18$
    $y = 4 - 2x$

3   $y = 3x + 11$
    $x + y = 3$

4   $y = 8 - 2x$
    $2x + 5y = 48$

5   $x = 3y - 5$
    $3x - 2y = 6$

6   $x - 2y = 7$
    $y = 3x + 4$

Exercise 15.2H

Solve these simultaneous equations algebraically.

1   $y + x - 3 = 0$
    $y = x^2 + 1$

2   $y = x^2 + x$
    $y = x + 1$

3   $y = x^2 + 3x - 1$
    $x - 2y - 4 = 0$

4   $y = 7x - 10$
    $y = x^2$

5   $x + y = 3$
    $4x - y^2 = 0$

6   $y = 4x + 3$
    $y = x^2 - 3x - 5$

7   $y - x = 5$
    $y = x^2 - 2x + 1$

8   $y = 2x^2 + 7x - 6$
    $y - 2x = 6$

Solve these simultaneous equations algebraically. Give your answers correct to 1 decimal place.

9   $y = 4x - 2$
    $y = x^2 + 3x - 5$

10 $y = 2x^2 + 7x$
    $y = 3x - 1$

Chapter 16 Trigonometry

Exercise 16.1H

1   Find the area of each of these triangles.

(a)

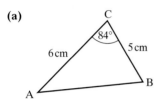

(b)

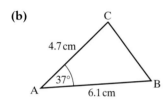

(c)

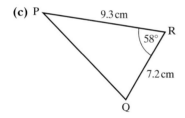

(d)

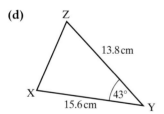

2   **(a)** In triangle ABC, $b = 9$ cm, $c = 16$ cm and the area is 60.4 cm^2.
    Find the size of angle A.
    (b) In triangle PQR, $q = 6.4$ cm, $r = 7.8$ cm and the area is 12.1 cm^2.
    Find the size of angle P.
    (c) In triangle XYZ, $x = 23.7$ cm, $y = 16.3$ cm and the area is 184 cm^2.
    Find the size of angle Z.

3   **(a)** In triangle ABC, $b = 20$ cm, angle C is 27° and the area is 145.3 cm^2.
    Find the length of side BC.
    (b) In triangle XYZ, $x = 9.3$ cm, angle Z is 94° and the area is 34.3 cm^2.
    Find the length of side XZ.

4   The area of triangle XYZ is 83 cm^2.
    Given that XY = 17.4 cm and angle XYZ = 63°, find YZ.

5   A triangle PQR has side PQ of length 5.2 cm, side QR of length 4.8 cm and an area of 11 cm^2.
    Calculate the size of angle PQR.

6   ABCD is a children's playground.
    OA = 83 m, OB = 122 m, OC = 106 m and OD = 78 m.

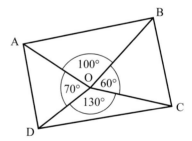

Calculate the area and the perimeter of the playground.
Give your answers to 3 significant figures.

Exercise 16.2H

1 Find the size of each of the sides and angles not given in these diagrams.

(a)

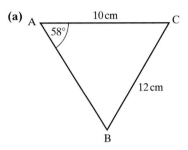

(b)

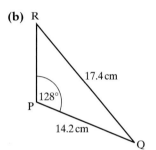

(c)

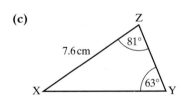

(d)

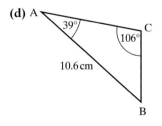

2 In triangle PQR, angle PQR is 38°, side PR is 8.3 cm and side PQ is 12 cm.
Calculate the size of the largest angle of the triangle.

3 P, Q and R are three buoys marking a sailing course.
The bearing of P from Q is 035°.
The bearing of P from R is 310°.
The bearing of R from Q is 075°.
The length of QR is 5.3 km.

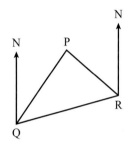

Find the total length of the three stages of the course from P back to P.

Exercise 16.3H

1 Find the size of each of the sides and angles marked in these diagrams.

(a)

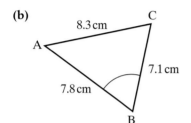

(b)

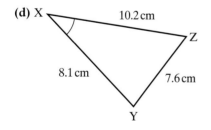

(c)

(d)

2 Find the size of each of the angles in these diagrams.

(a)

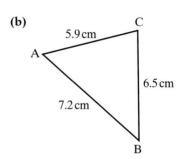

(b)

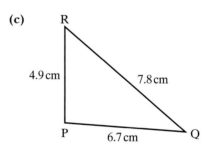

(c)

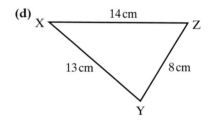

(d)

3 ABCDEFGH is a cuboid.
ACH is a triangle contained within the cuboid.

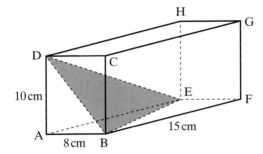

Calculate the size of these angles.
(a) Angle BDE
(b) Angle BED

4 A, B and C are points on an orienteering course.
The bearing of B from A is 040°.
The bearing of C from B is 125°.
AB is 3.7 km and BC is 2.3 km.

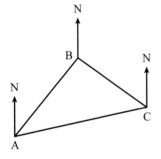

How long is AC?

Exercise 16.4H

1 (a) Draw accurately the graph of $y = \sin\theta$ for values of θ from −180° to 180°.
(b) For what values of θ in this range does $\sin\theta = 0.7$?

2 (a) Draw accurately the graph of $y = \cos\theta$ for values of θ from 0° to 360°.
(b) For what values of θ in this range does $\cos\theta = -0.6$?

3 (a) Draw accurately the graph of $y = \sin\theta$ for values of θ from 0° to 360°.
(b) From your graph read off all the values of θ for which $\sin\theta = -0.8$.

4 (a) Draw accurately the graph of $y = \cos\theta$ for values of θ from −180° to 360°.
(b) From your graph read off all the values of θ for which $\cos\theta = -0.3$.

5 One solution to $\sin\theta = 0.6$ is approximately 37°. Using only the symmetry of the sine curve, find the other angles between −180° and 540° that also satisfy the equation $\sin\theta = 0.6$.

6 (a) Draw accurately the graph of $y = \tan\theta$ for values of θ from −180° to 360°.
(b) Find, from your graph, the angles for which $\tan\theta = -1.5$.

Exercise 16.5H

1 Find the amplitude and the period of each of these curves.
(a) $y = 2\sin\theta$
(b) $y = \cos 4\theta$
(c) $y = 5\sin 2\theta$
(d) $y = 3\sin 0.8\theta$
(e) $y = 4\cos 5\theta$
(f) $y = 7\cos 0.6\theta$

2 Draw the graph of $y = 2\cos\theta$ for values of θ from 0° to 360°.

3 Draw the graph of $y = \sin 3\theta$ for values of θ from −180° to 180°.

4 Sketch the graph of $y = \cos 5\theta$ for values of θ from 0° to 360°.

5 Sketch the graph of $y = 1.5\sin\theta$ for values of θ from −180° to 180°.

6 Find the solutions of $\cos 4\theta = -0.6$ between 0° and 360°.

Chapter 17 Functions

Exercise 17.1H

1 $f(x) = x^2 + 4$
Find the value of each of these.
(a) $f(3)$ **(b)** $f(-2)$

2 $g(x) = x^2 + 2x + 1$
Find the value of each of these.
(a) $g(3)$ **(b)** $g(-2)$ **(c)** $g(0)$

3 $h(x) = 5x - 3$
(a) Solve $h(x) = 7$.
(b) Write an expression for each of these.
(i) $h(x - 2)$ **(ii)** $h(2x)$

4 $f(x) = 2x + 4$
(a) Solve $f(x) = 1$.
(b) Write an expression for each of these.
(i) $2f(x)$ **(ii)** $f(2x + 3)$

5 $g(x) = 5x - 3$
(a) Solve $g(x) = 0$
(b) Write an expression for each of these.
(i) $g(x + 3)$ **(ii)** $2g(x) + 3$

6 $h(x) = x^2 + 2$
(a) Solve $h(x) = 6$.
(b) Write an expression for each of these.
(i) $h(x + 3)$ **(ii)** $h(2x) + 1$

7 $f(x) = 2x^2 - 3x$
(a) Find the value of $f(-2)$.
(b) Write an expression for each of these.
(i) $f(x + 2)$ **(ii)** $f(3x)$

8 $g(x) = x^2 + 3x$
(a) Solve $g(x) = -2$.
(b) Write an expression for each of these.
(i) $3g(x) + 4$ **(ii)** $g(2x + 1)$

Exercise 17.2H

1 **(a)** Sketch these graphs on the same diagram.
(i) $y = -x^2$ **(ii)** $y = 2 - x^2$
(b) State the transformation that maps
$y = -x^2$ on to $y = 2 - x^2$.

2 **(a)** Sketch these graphs on the same diagram.
(i) $y = x^2$ **(ii)** $y = x^2 - 4$
(b) State the transformation that maps $y = x^2$ on to $y = x^2 - 4$.

3 **(a)** Sketch these graphs on the same diagram.
(i) $y = x^2$
(ii) $y = (x - 2)^2$
(iii) $y = (x - 2)^2 + 3$
(b) State the transformation that maps $y = x^2$ on to $y = (x - 2)^2 + 3$.

4 **(a)** Sketch the result of translating the graph
of $y = \cos\theta$ by $\begin{pmatrix} 0 \\ 2 \end{pmatrix}$.
(b) State the equation of the transformed graph.

5 State the equation of the curve which is the translation of $y = \tan\theta$ by these vectors.
(a) $\begin{pmatrix} 0 \\ 4 \end{pmatrix}$ **(b)** $\begin{pmatrix} 3 \\ 0 \end{pmatrix}$

6 The diagram shows the graph of $y = f(x)$.

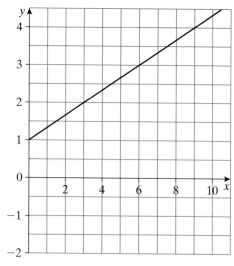

Copy the diagram and draw these graphs on the same axes.
(a) $y = f(x) - 3$
(b) $y = f(x - 3)$

7 The diagram shows the graph of $y = g(x)$.

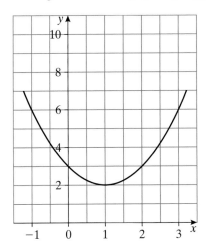

Copy the diagram and draw these graphs on the same axes.
(a) $y = g(x - 1)$
(b) $y = g(x) - 2$

8 State the equation of the curve which is the translation of $y = x^2$ by $\begin{pmatrix} 3 \\ -4 \end{pmatrix}$.

9 This is the graph of a transformed sine curve.

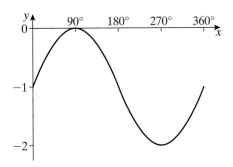

State its equation.

10 The graph of $y = x^2 + 3x$ is translated by $\begin{pmatrix} 2 \\ 3 \end{pmatrix}$.

(a) State the equation of the transformed graph.
(b) Show that this equation can be written as $y = x^2 - x + 1$.

11 (a) Write the equation $y = x^2 - 8x + 19$ in the form $y = (x + a)^2 + b$ by completing the square.
(b) Use your answer to part **(a)** to describe the transformation that maps $y = x^2$ on to $y = x^2 - 8x + 19$.
(c) Describe the transformation that maps $y = x^2$ on to $y = x^2 + 4x - 3$.

Exercise 17.3H

1 (a) Sketch on the same axes the graphs of $y = \cos\theta$ and $y = 2\cos\theta$ for $0° \leqslant \theta \leqslant 360°$.
(b) Describe the transformation that maps $y = \cos\theta$ on to $y = 2\cos\theta$.

2 (a) Sketch on the same axes the graphs of $y = \sin\theta$ and $y = \sin 2\theta$ for $0° \leqslant \theta \leqslant 360°$.
(b) Describe the transformation that maps $y = \sin\theta$ on to $y = \sin 2\theta$.

3 Describe the transformation that maps
(a) $y = \sin\theta + 1$ on to $y = \sin(-\theta) + 1$.
(b) $y = x^2 + 2$ on to $y = -x^2 - 2$.
(c) $y = x^2$ on to $y = 3x^2$.
(d) $y = \sin\theta$ on to $y = \sin\dfrac{\theta}{3}$.

4 The graph of $y = \sin\theta$ is transformed by a one-way stretch parallel to the θ-axis with a scale factor of $\frac{1}{4}$.
State the equation of the resulting graph.

5 State the equation of the graph $y = x^2 - 1$ after each of these transformations.
(a) A reflection in the y-axis
(b) A reflection in the x-axis

6 State the equation of the graph of $y = 4x + 1$ after each of these transformations.
(a) A one-way stretch parallel to the y-axis with a scale factor of 4
(b) A one-way stretch parallel to the x-axis with a scale factor of $\frac{1}{2}$

7 Describe the transformation that maps $y = f(x)$ on to each of these graphs.
(a) $y = f(x) - 2$ **(b)** $y = 3f(x)$
(c) $y = f(0.5x)$ **(d)** $y = 4f(2x)$

8 Find the equation of the graph of $y = x^2 + 3$ after each of these transformations.
   (a) A reflection in the x-axis
   (b) A reflection in the y-axis
   (c) A one-way stretch parallel to the x-axis with a scale factor of 0.5

 9 The graph of $y = x^2 - 2x$ is stretched parallel to the x-axis by a scale factor of 2.
   (a) State the equation of the resulting graph.
   (b) What does the point $(1, -1)$ map on to under this transformation?

 10 The equation of this graph is $y = a \sin b\theta$.

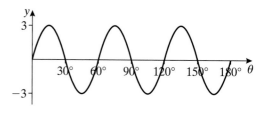

Find a and b.

Length, area and volume

Exercise 18.1H

1   Find the arc length of each of these sectors.
    Give your answers to the nearest millimetre.

(a)

6.7 cm   42°   6.7 cm

(b)

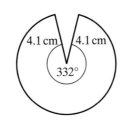

4.1 cm   4.1 cm

332°

(c)

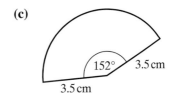

152°   3.5 cm

3.5 cm

2   Find the area of each of the sectors in question **1**.

3   Find the sector angle of each of these sectors.
    Give your answers to the nearest degree.

(a)

5 cm

5 cm   5 cm

(b)

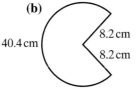

40.4 cm   8.2 cm

8.2 cm

(c)

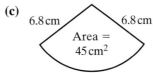

6.8 cm   6.8 cm

Area =
45 cm²

(d)

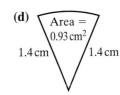

Area =
0.93 cm²

1.4 cm   1.4 cm

4   Find the radius of each of these sectors.

(a)

5.3 cm

48°

(b)

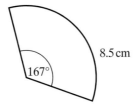

8.5 cm

167°

(c)

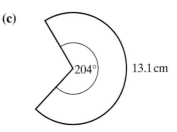

204°   13.1 cm

5   Find the radius of each of these sectors.

(a)

Area =
16.1 cm²

72°

(b)

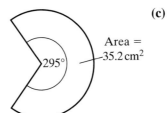

295°

Area =
35.2 cm²

(c)

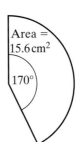

Area =
15.6 cm²

170°

6 A sector of a circle of radius 5.1 cm has an area of 38 cm².
Calculate the angle of the sector and hence find the arc length of the sector.

 7 A decorative frieze is made with alternating
sectors as shown.
The radius of each sector is 75 cm and the sector
angle is 150°.
Calculate the area in square metres covered by the
seven sectors shown.
Give your answer to 3 significant figures.

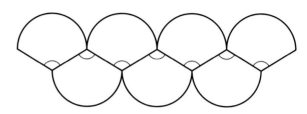

 8 A piece of wire of length 20 cm is bent into a circular arc.
(a) The angle at the centre is 30°.
What is the radius of the arc?

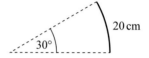

(b) The same piece of wire is now bent into a circular
arc with a radius of 20 cm.
What is the angle at the centre?

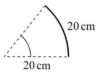

9 A rose bed, which is set in a lawn, is in the shape of a sector of a circle with an angle of 125° and a
radius of 7 m.
(a) The gardener is trimming the lawn edge round the rose bed.
Calculate the total distance he has to cut.
(b) The gardener wants to spread rose fertiliser over the rose bed.
Calculate the area that needs to be covered.
Give your answers to an appropriate degree of accuracy.

Exercise 18.2H

1 Find the curved surface area of each of these cones.
Give your answers to 3 significant figures.

(a) 12.5 cm 10.0 cm 7.5 cm

(b) 12.0 cm 12.5 cm 3.5 cm

(c) 7.2 cm 7.8 cm 3.0 cm

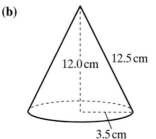

2 Calculate the volume of each of the cones in question **1**.

3 Calculate the volume of each of these square- or rectangular–based pyramids.

(a)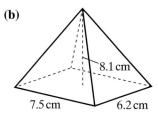

8 cm

6 cm   6 cm

(b)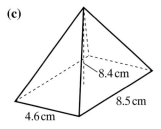

8.1 cm

7.5 cm   6.2 cm

(c)

8.4 cm

8.5 cm

4.6 cm

4 A solid cone has a base of radius 6.1 cm and a slant height of 8.4 cm.
   Calculate its total surface area.

5 A pyramid has a rectangular base of sides 4.5 cm and 6.0 cm.
   Its volume is 73.8 cm^3.
   Find its height.

6 Find the radius of the base of each of these cones.
   (a) Volume 256 cm^3, height 7.8 cm
   (b) Volume 343 cm^3, height 6.5 cm
   (c) Volume 192 cm^3, height 10.4 cm

7 A sector of a circle is joined to form a cone.
   Find the radius of the base of the cone made with each of these sectors.
   (a) Radius 8.1 cm, angle 150°
   (b) Radius 10.8 cm, angle 315°
   (c) Radius 7.2 cm, angle 247°

8 Find the surface area of each of these spheres.
   (a) Radius 3.6 cm
   (b) Radius 8.5 cm
   (c) Diameter 36 cm

9 Find the volumes of each of the spheres in question **8**.

10 Find the radius of each of these spheres.
   (a) Surface area 650 cm^2 **(b)** Surface area 270 cm^2
   (c) Volume 1820 cm^3 **(d)** Volume 3840 cm^3

11 This cyclindrical jug holds 1 litre.
   Its base radius is 4 cm.
   Find its height.

12 This conical glass holds 150 ml.
Its top radius is 4 cm.
Find its depth, *d*.

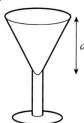

13 A glass vase is in the shape of a cylinder with a base.
Its external height is 25 cm and its external diameter is 10 cm.
The thickness of the glass is 5 mm.
Find the volume of glass in the vase.

14 A metal sphere of radius 4 cm is melted down and then cast as a cube.
What are the dimensions of the cube?

Exercise 18.3H

1 Calculate the area of each of the shaded segments.

(a)

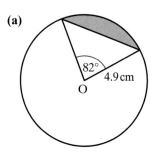

(b)

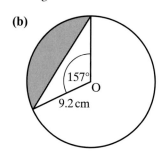

(c)

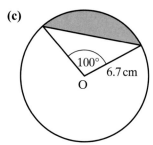

2 A concrete gate-post is in the shape of a
cuboid 1.6 m by 30 cm by 30 cm topped
with a sphere of radius 12 cm.
Calculate the volume of the gate-post.

3 Calculate the area of each of the shaded major segments.

(a)

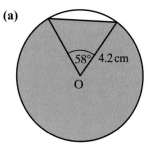

(b)

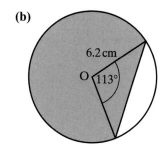

(c)

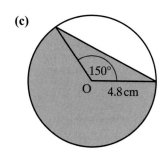

4 A birthday cake has a radius of 9 cm and a height of 8 cm.
Its top and sides are covered in icing.
Marie is given a slice of the cake.
It is a sector of angle 50°.
Calculate the surface area of the icing on Marie's slice of cake.

5 Calculate the perpendicular height of each of these cones and hence find their volumes.

(a)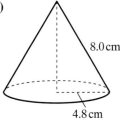
8.0 cm

4.8 cm

(b)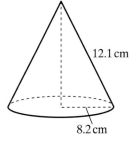
12.1 cm

8.2 cm

(c)
11.8 cm

10.1 cm

6 A solid cone has a base of radius 7.9 cm and a height of 11.8 cm.
(a) Calculate its volume.
(b) Find its slant height and hence its total surface area.

7 The top half in height of a cone is removed.
Show that the volume of the remaining frustum is $\frac{7}{8}$ of the volume of the original cone.
What fraction of the original curved surface area of the cone is the curved surface area of the frustum?

8 A podium is a frustum of a cone. The height of the frustum is 1.2 m and the diameters of its top and its base
are 0.8 m and 1.4 m respectively.
(a) Show that the podium is a frustum of a cone of complete height 2.8 m.
(b) Calculate the volume of the podium.

9 A pyramid has a square base of side 12.8 cm and its volume is 524 cm³.
(a) Calculate its height.
(b) Hence show that the sloping edges (which are all of equal length) are 13.2 cm long.

10 A lampshade is made from a piece of parchment.

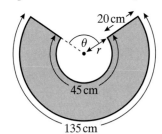
20 cm
θ
r
45 cm
135 cm

(a) Find, in the form $\dfrac{k}{\pi}$, the angle θ.
(b) Hence calculate the surface area of the lampshade.

UNIT

C

11 A cylindrical glass bowl of radius 15 cm has water in it with floating candles.
20 glass marbles of radius 1.2 cm are placed in the bowl.

By how much does the water level in the bowl increase?

12 A cone has a base of radius 4.3 cm and height of 8.4 cm.
It has the same volume as a sphere.
Find the radius of the sphere.

13 A hemispherical glass bowl has an internal diameter of 22 cm and is 7.5 mm thick throughout.
5% of the original glass is removed when a pattern is cut into the bowl.
Calculate the volume of glass remaining.

14 A salt pot is in the form of a hollow cylinder of diameter 3 cm and height 3 cm with a hemispherical shell fixed on top.
Salt is poured into the pot to a depth of 2.5 cm.
The pot in inverted, with the hole covered, so the flat base of the cylinder is horizontal.

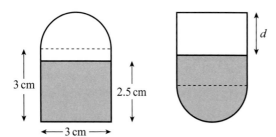

Find the distance, d, from the top of the salt to the flat base of the cylinder.

Exercise 19.1H

1 A bag contains five red counters, three green counters and two yellow counters.
What is the probability of selecting
(a) a red counter or a green counter?
(b) a green counter or a yellow counter?

2 When Mr Smith goes on holiday the probability that he goes to the seaside is 0.4, to the countryside is 0.35 and to a city is 0.25.
What is the probability that he goes on holiday
(a) to the countryside or the city?
(b) to the seaside or the city?

3 A spinner is numbered 1 to 5.
The probabilities of each of the numbers occurring are given in the table.

Number	1	2	3	4	5
Probability	0.39	0.14	0.22	0.11	0.14

What is the probability that in one spin the number will be
(a) 1 or 2?   **(b)** 3, 4 or 5?
(c) an odd number?   **(d)** less than 2?
(e) at least 3?

4 There are four kings and four aces in a pack of 52 playing cards.
A card is chosen at random.
What is the probability that it is a king or an ace?

5 A coin is tossed and a dice is thrown.
What is the probability of getting a head on the coin and an even number on the dice?

6 An ordinary dice is thrown three times.
What is the probability that the dice lands on 6 each time?

7 The probability that the school team wins their next hockey match is 0.8.
What is the probability that, in their next two matches, the school team
(a) wins both matches?
(b) wins neither match?

8 Each of the letters of the word MISSISSIPPI is written on a card.
The cards are shuffled and one is selected.
This card is returned to the pack which is again shuffled.
A second card is selected.
What is the probability that the two cards are
(a) both P?
(b) both S?
(c) both a consonant?

9 A box contains a large number of red beads and a large number of white beads.
40% of the beads are red.
A bead is chosen from the box, its colour is noted and it is replaced.
A second bead is then chosen.
What is the probability that
(a) both beads are red?
(b) both beads are white?
(c) one bead of each colour is chosen?

10 In a large batch of lightbulbs, the probability that a bulb is defective is 0.01.
Three lightbulbs are selected at random for testing.
What is the probability that
(a) all three work?
(b) all three are defective?
(c) two of the three are defective?

Exercise 19.2H

1 Pat is playing a board game with a spinner numbered 1 to 4.
She spins the spinner twice.
(a) Copy and complete the tree diagram.

```
First        Second
spin          spin     Outcome   Probability
                  Four          FF
        Four  <
                  Not a         FN
                  four

                  Four          NF
        Not a <
        four      Not a         NN
                  four
```

(b) Use the tree diagram to work out the probability that
(i) Pat gets two 4s.
(ii) Pat gets just one 4.

2 The probability that I get up late on any day is 0.3.
(a) Draw a tree diagram to show my getting up late or not late on two days.
(b) Work out the probability that
(i) I don't get up late on either of the two days.
(ii) I get up late on one of the two days.

3 There are five red discs and three blue discs in a bag.
A disc is selected, its colour is noted and it is then replaced in the bag.
A second disc is then selected.
(a) Draw a probability tree diagram to show the outcomes of the two selections.
(b) Use the tree diagram to find the probability that
(i) both discs are red.
(ii) both discs are the same colour.
(iii) at least one disc is blue.

4 The probabilities that Phil wins, draws or loses any game of chess are 0.6, 0.3 and 0.1 respectively.
(a) Draw a tree diagram to show the outcomes of Phil's next two games.
(b) Work out the probability that
(i) Phil wins both games.
(ii) Phil wins one of the two games.
(iii) the results of the two games are the same.

5 On the way to work, Beverley passes through three sets of traffic lights.
The probability that the first set of lights is green when she reaches them is 0.6.
The probability that the second set is green is 0.7.
The probability that the third set is green is 0.8.
(a) Draw a probability tree diagram to show the possible outcomes.
(b) What is the probability that she has to stop at
(i) all three sets of lights?
(ii) just one set of lights?
(iii) at least two sets of lights?

6 Paul and Kate and playing a game using two five-sided spinners, each numbered 1 to 5.
A player needs to spin the spinners and get a 'double' to start.
(a) Find the probability that Paul only starts on his third spin.
(b) Write down an expression in terms of n for the probability that Kate starts on her nth spin.

Exercise 19.3H

1 There are four black beads and three white beads in a box.
   A bead is selected at random and not replaced.
   A second bead is then selected.
   (a) Draw a probability tree diagram to show all the possible outcomes.
   (b) Find the probability that the two beads are
      (i)   both white.
      (ii) one of each colour.

2 Ben randomly selects three cards, without replacing any, from a normal pack of 52 playing cards.
   What is the probability that
   (a) all three are aces?
   (b) two of the three are aces?

3 The probability of it snowing one day in winter is reported to be 0.2.
   If it snows on that day, the probability that it snows the following day is 0.7.
   If it doesn't snow, the probability that it will snow the following day is 0.1.
   (a) Draw a probability tree diagram to show the possible outcomes.
   (b) What is the probability of
      (i)   it snowing on both days?
      (ii) it not snowing on both days?
      (iii) it snowing on at least one of the two days?

4 When Elaine goes to school, she either walks, cycles or goes by bus.
   The probability that she walks is 0.5 and that she cycles is 0.2.
   If she walks the probability that she is late is 0.4, if she cycles it is 0.1 and if she goes by bus it is 0.2.
   What is the probability that she is late for school?

5 There are nine boys and fifteen girls in a class.
   Three children are to be randomly selected to represent the class in a competition.
   What is the probability that
   (a) all three are girls?
   (b) one is a girl and two are boys?
   (c) at least two girls are chosen?

 6 Some Professional exams consist of two parts: Part 1 and Part 2.
   Candidates take Part 1 first.
   If they fail Part 1 they are not allowed to take Part 2.
   Thomas has been practising by doing past papers and he is about to take the exams.
   The probability that he will pass Part 1 is 0.85.
   The probability that he will pass Part 2 is 0.75.
   Calculate the probability that Thomas will fail the exams.

Algebraic fractions

Exercise 20.1H

Simplify these.

1. $\dfrac{x+4}{3} + \dfrac{x-1}{2}$

2. $\dfrac{x+5}{3} - \dfrac{x+3}{4}$

3. $\dfrac{x-3}{2} - \dfrac{x-5}{3}$

4. $\dfrac{4x+3}{2} - \dfrac{3x-2}{4}$

5. $\dfrac{2}{x+3} + \dfrac{x-1}{3}$

6. $\dfrac{2}{x-5} + \dfrac{x+4}{2}$

7. $\dfrac{3x+4}{5} - \dfrac{3}{2x-1}$

8. $\dfrac{5x+4}{3x-2} + \dfrac{5}{4}$

Exercise 20.2H

Simplify these.

1. $\dfrac{3}{x+2} + \dfrac{2}{x-1}$

2. $\dfrac{4}{x-3} + \dfrac{x+3}{2x}$

3. $\dfrac{x+5}{2x} - \dfrac{3x}{x+2}$

4. $\dfrac{x+5}{x-3} - \dfrac{x-3}{x+2}$

5. $\dfrac{1}{x+4} - \dfrac{3}{x-5}$

6. $\dfrac{x}{x-3} + \dfrac{x-2}{x+1}$

7. $\dfrac{3x+2}{x-5} - \dfrac{x-3}{x-4}$

8. $\dfrac{2x+3}{3x+1} - \dfrac{x-2}{2x+5}$

Exercise 20.3H

Solve these.

1. $\dfrac{x-3}{2} - \dfrac{x-2}{3} = 1$

2. $\dfrac{5}{x-5} = \dfrac{3}{x-2}$

3. $\dfrac{1}{4x-3} = \dfrac{1}{3x+2}$

4. $\dfrac{3-x}{4} + \dfrac{2x+5}{3} = 1$

5. $\dfrac{x-2}{5} - \dfrac{2x-3}{4} = \dfrac{1}{3}$

6. $\dfrac{3x}{x+4} + \dfrac{2x}{5x-2} = \dfrac{3}{2}$

7. $\dfrac{2}{3x+1} - \dfrac{5}{x+3} = 0$

8. $\dfrac{3}{x-2} - \dfrac{1}{x+1} = 1$